D1334435

SOUNDMAKING

Publication Number 538

AMERICAN LECTURE SERIES®

A Monograph in

The BANNERSTONE DIVISION *of*
AMERICAN LECTURES IN COMMUNICATION

Edited by

DOMINICK A. BARBARA, M.D., F.A.P.A.
Head of the Speech Department
Karen Horney Clinic
New York City

SOUNDMAKING

The Acoustic Communication of Emotion

PETER F. OSTWALD, M.D.

Assistant Clinical Professor of Psychiatry
University of California School of Medicine

Attending Psychiatrist
Langley Porter Neuropsychiatric Institute
San Francisco, California

CHARLES C THOMAS · PUBLISHER

Springfield · Illinois · U.S.A.

Published and Distributed Throughout the World by
CHARLES C THOMAS • PUBLISHER
BANNERSTONE HOUSE
301-327 East Lawrence Avenue, Springfield, Illinois, U.S.A.

With THOMAS BOOKS careful attention is given to all details of manufacturing and design. It is the Publisher's desire to present books that are satisfactory as to their physical qualities and artistic possibilities and appropriate for their particular use. THOMAS BOOKS will be true to those laws of quality that assure a good name and good will.

Printed in the United States of America

PREFACE

During a psychiatric research seminar with Drs. Jurgen Ruesch and Herbert Lehmann in 1958 I decided to embark on a study of soundmaking, a subject that always has both fascinated and terrified me. I reviewed the literature then available (90)* but decided against adopting any of the standard approaches to soundmaking, since each served to pull the subject-matter too much out of the framework of psychopathology in which I was most interested. Acoustics stressed the physical nature of sound; linguistics focussed on formal aspects of speech; music dealt with specialized instrumental and vocal forms of soundmaking; medicine treated the lungs, larynx, cochlea, and other isolated body parts.

Shortly after this I had the good fortune to meet Dr. Walter Rosenblith at the Massachusetts Institute of Technology. He called my attention to the investigations of R. G. Busnel, and to other interesting work in the newly-developing field of Bio-acoustics. This encouraged me to try using similar methods for psychiatric research. Some results have already been published in various scientific journals, and when Dr. Barbara invited me to contribute to the American Lecture Series in Communication I seized upon the opportunity to present my current research in book form. I hope that this material will interest psychiatrists, speech therapists, linguists, music teachers, and anyone else whose job is the analysis and improvement of human sound-making.

I am grateful to Mr. George Wilson, who taught me how to measure sounds, and to Dr. Walter Soroka, who allowed me to conduct preliminary studies in the Acoustical Laboratory of the University of California, Berkeley. Since September 1959, I have

---

*Numbers in parentheses pertain to references listed in the Bibliography on page 159.

v

worked in the Research Department of the Langley Porter Neuro-psychiatric Institute, where Drs. Enoch Callaway III, John Stark-weather, and William Hargreaves gave me help and critical guidance. Dr. Joseph Biernoff aided me with the clinical problems discussed in this book, and Dr. William Shipley showed me how to use linguistic transcription. Others who have been directly helpful are Drs. Alexander Simon, Stanislaus Szurek, Paul Moses, and Richard Flower. Mrs. Bernice Engle helped me with writing, and Mr. Sanford Autumn did the statistical work. Mr. Robert Wong made the graphs and Mrs. Carol Parker typed the final manuscript for this book.

A Fellowship Grant from the Foundations' Fund for Research in Psychiatry enabled me to conduct much of the research presented in this book and to prepare the material for publication.

PETER F. OSTWALD

CONTENTS

INTRODUCTION

That soundmaking is an activity as necessary to human survival and comfort as are breathing, feeding, sleeping, and other vital processes is the theme of this book and its point of departure from more formal treatises in acoustics, phonetics, musicology, and related subjects. I consider even the noises which inevitably accompany those physiologic activities enumerated above to be more than just accidental byproducts of behavior. Every physician who has used a stethoscope knows that the sounds of the body are informative signals — sent out unintentionally, yes — but nonetheless meaningful to an experienced listener. So it is also with crying, laughter, and various other sounds of emotional expression. Music, speech, and organized noise are culturally conditioned forms of soundmaking; but also these communications carry information about the soundmaker's emotions, no matter how carefully he tries to hide them behind the acoustic symbols he emits (92).

Psychiatrists, more than any other medical specialists, must understand soundmaking, since what we regard as psychopathology is more often communicated acoustically than visually. Also our psychotherapeutic influence is exerted primarily through speech, silence, sighing, hmms, ohs, and other acoustic signals. How this comes about is very puzzling, and within recent years the question has led to increasingly incisive investigations (110), as well as a considerable amount of important collaboration between different scientific disciplines. An encounter between psychiatry and linguistics was bonded through the friendship of Harry Stack Sullivan with Edward Sapir (129), and today's microlinguistic approach to psychiatric interview material offers an intriguing way for studying acoustic communication of emotion in all its complexity (101). Psychiatry and acoustics have not yet had too much to do with each other. Psychoacoustics concentrates on normal soundmaking (127) and has so far left the acoustics of mental illness to clinicians. Consequently almost every psychiatric textbook describes patients as sounding anxious, depressed, whiny, insincere, etc. without ever indicating what the acoustic concomitants of these emotional states might be. It is even more unforgivable that while texts generally encourage acoustic communication with patients, they emphasize the denotative aspects of this behavior—the *what* to talk about—and tend all but to ignore the emotional implications of soundmaking. I think that the practical problem of community noise control will ultimately force acousticians to become better acquainted with psychiatrists. In any event an encouraging sign is a recent new journal brought out by the Acoustical Society of America, *Sound —Its Uses and Control.*

The present book is organized in such a way that the reader goes step-by-step from a general discussion of historical trends in soundmaking to the specific consideration of psychopathologic problems in acoustic communication. The first chapter emphasizes music, which is the kind of sound that has been most systematically studied by historians. Chapter 2 deals with the relationships between animal soundmaking, human preverbal behavior, and speech. I have chosen to set forth only those aspects of this problem which pertain directly to subsequent chapters, and try to make clear that no hard-and-fast boundaries between animal, baby, and adult sounds actually exist.

Chapter 3 is a condensed introduction to problems of acoustic denotation. Descriptive, visual, and measurement approaches are briefly summarized. For a full and more balanced understanding of this difficult area in soundmaking research, the reader must consult references cited in the bibliography. A scanner need look only at illustrations one through five to get the gist of this chapter. To comprehend the methods used throughout the rest of the book it will be helpful to read the last part of this chapter, called "acoustic measurement."

The next two chapters compare, by means of acoustic analyses, the sounds of preverbal crying and of verbal speech. Chapter 4 takes the baby cry as a prototypal alarm signal, demonstrates some of its acoustic properties, and begins to relate these to characteristics of the sender and to reactions of the listener. Chapter 5 turns to the sound of speech and introduces the concept of motants, which I find helpful in thinking about the possible acoustic formant structure of emotive sounds.

The rest of the book deals acoustically and descriptively with various clinical problems. Chapter 6 studies four stereotyped forms of soundmaking found among psychiatric patients. Chapter 7 traces the acoustic productions of one patient in psychotherapy through eleven consecutive interviews. Chapter 8 shows in a more systematic fashion how changes in the acoustic output of human beings may be related to nonacoustic behavior variables. Chapter 9 turns to the listener and investigates some of his reactions to the sounds of babies. Not being an experimental psychologist I have undoubtedly committed many errors in conducting the experiments reported here. But they are presented anyway, because I am convinced of the need for such studies and because I hope that this may also stimulate others to study the communicative potentials of nonverbal sounds.

Chapter 10 presents four patients who cannot speak. No attempt is made to detail the history and psychopathology in every case. Rather the emphasis here is on an underlying defect in communication—the inability to use sounds symbolically—which seems to unite these patients from different diagnostic groups into one acoustic syndrome. Chapter 11 is concerned with speech pathology, and like the preceding clinical discussion eschews official terminology in favor of an approach focussing on soundmaking. This serves to point out, I hope, that all the patients presented suffer from an inability to distinguish between emotive and denotative soundmaking.

At the end of each chapter is a brief summary which gives the essence of what has gone before and occasionally adds a new idea that may not have been previously discussed but seemed pertinent for consideration at the time. Also there is a Coda (in lieu of a Conclusion, which would have been inappropriate considering the exploratory nature of this research) at the end of the book in order to provide a few suggestions for future investigations in the field of acoustic communication of emotions. Since I have used some terms that may be unfamiliar to readers or ambiguous in certain contexts, I try to define these as best I can in the Glossary on page 167. Most of the references in the Bibliography provide background information for specific ideas and problems presented in the following chapters. I have also cited several works of more general interest which I think ought to be looked into in order to get a deeper understanding of the issues behind this research, in particular Langer's *Philosophy in a New Key* (70), Sorokin's tremendous opus on *Forms of Art* (121), and the important theoretical papers by Ruesch (108) and Kris (67).

SOUNDMAKING

Chapter 1

HISTORICAL PERSPECTIVES

Man is by nature a soundmaker. He has a throat and a mouth admirably suited for crying, produces acoustic signals the moment he is born, and later makes communicative noises with his hands, feet, toys, and tools (106). These sounds serve different purposes at various times: people make sounds to alert one another; they organize their activities by means of acoustic stimuli; they exchange messages with sounds encoded into words; they make sounds for entertainment, for love, and for combat. The history of soundmaking therefore parallels that of civilization itself, and comprises phases from the evolution of music, language, weaponry, medicine, acoustics, and psychology.

According to the findings of archeologists, man has used soundmaking instruments—hollow logs, stone rattles, and other noisy objects—since his first days on earth (111). But it seems that at the dawn of civilization, man could not recognize any of his own sounds to be products of human activity; instead he attributed acoustic phenomena to divine origins. Given to mystical speculation, the ancients apparently thought sound to be some sort of powerful and indestructible substance animating everything which moves. For instance according to primitive folklore, the *noise* made by a man's spear on impact with an animal or human enemy contains a death-dealing power which deprives the victim of life. It is the *roar* of the waterfall that supposedly holds energies causing the earth to tremble. Sounds were said to influence the growth of plants, change the seasons, and stop the sun in its course (27).

Even after the birth of civilization, man continued to credit imaginary beings with the power and willfulness that sounds were thought to possess. For instance, the Assyrians felt that evil deities called *Ea* and *Ramman* produce dreaded nature sounds which supposedly caused earthquakes, thunder, and storms. Also selfproduced sounds were attributed to mythical entities. The Mesopotamians for example, held the goddess *Ishtar* responsible for music which man himself made on reed pipes; and her partner *Tammuz* was credited with the "tender voice of song (112)."

A more realistic acoustical attitude developed as people banded closer together and leaders emerged to direct their organized activity. Practical men now began to use the supposedly godgiven powers of sound for strategic purposes. Egyptian generals, for example, cunningly excited the men under their command by using trumpet calls and drum beats. These acoustic devices served readily to summon the warriors to assigned meeting places, to improve their morale, and to stimulate their greed for combat. Deliberate soundmaking appeared also in nondestructive human activities such as religious festivals, medicine, and erotic life (13). During the Greek era physicians came to recognize certain physiological facts about sound. Hippocrates (460-370 B.C.) described different respiratory noises by putting his ear against the human chest; he visualized the eardrum and postulated an echo theory about the phenomena of hearing (9).

Scientific study of acoustics also originated in Greece. Pythagoras of Samos (582-507 B.C.) plucked strings and observed that the length of the vibrating portion bore a definite numerical relationship to the pitch sensation produced in the listener's ear from the resulting sound. His important experiments—and the theories which sprang from them—permanently marked the history of Western science and have influenced acoustical work up to the present time. The Pythagoreans proved physical stimuli to bring about sound sensations; they thereby established a precedent for dealing with sounds in terms of actual origins and by means of measurement (9).

These early acousticians were philosophers as well as scientists. An explanation merely of the physical vibration patterns of acoustic stimuli failed to satisfy their thirst for deeper understanding. Knowing certain sounds to produce intensely pleasurable experiences and others to be unpleasant, the Greeks embedded acoustical facts into elaborate abstract theories about harmony, order, and beauty (55). This led ultimately to complex cosmological ideas, such as the notion about "music of the spheres" which later intrigued medieval astronomers (65).

The Romans exploited acoustics and expanded many of the already established uses of soundmaking. Two organs for music were found in the ruins of Pompeii, and a Roman theater at Nora near the southern coast of Sardinia has a loudspeaker system consisting of four megaphones five feet long and close to four feet wide (99). Roman armies engaged musicians to deceive enemy troops by making misleading noises in abandoned camps. The emperor Nero (A.D. 37-68), himself a trained musician, had a claque of 5,000 persons as noisemakers in public meetings to influence the behavior of the crowds. Three distinct forms of applause were used, depending on the desired effects: *bombi,* like buzzing of bees; *imbrices,* like rain or hail on a roof; and *testae,* like pots crashing (114).

Collapse of the Roman Empire probably brought much of the scientific study of acoustic problems to an end, and for some time soundmaking became mainly a matter for practitioners. Priests, musicians, and doctors performed their duties, while trying also to teach their acoustical art to others. Demonstrations and word-of-mouth had to suffice, since professional soundmakers were usually too busy, too illiterate, or too persecuted to write down what they knew. Devoid of rules and organized knowledge, soundmaking followed no certain directions, until original ways of singing were tried out in churches. Now Catholic leaders became concerned with soundmaking, and Pope Gregory I (A.D. 540-604) ruled that only certain tonal progressions called modes be permitted in church. This codification of modal scales set a unique trend for soundmaking in the Western World, one which led ultimately to that refinement of acoustic technique and compositorial virtuosity known as classical music (31).

But the Gregorian tradition which molded music also reinforced an artificial dichotomy in Western thinking about sounds —a tendency to needlessly divide soundmaking into fictitious "opposites" like classical and popular, ecclesiastic and secular, formal and informal, elegant and slang, meaningful and meaningless. An interesting example of this, which is still prevalent today and is found in every acoustic text, has to do with the arbitrary distinction between "low" and "high" pitch (see Chapter 3). During the 12th Century "low instruments" were recognized to be softsounding, and became especially popular among people of refined taste in France, until the advent of violinplaying in the 17th Century. "High instruments" were considered more noisy and louder; they were preferably played in open air and came to symbolize peasants, secular affairs, and cruder aspects of life. The violin was even thought of as the devil's instrument (100).

While naturalistic trends during the Renaissance unsettled some of these prejudices about sounds, the Puritan movement rendered certain forms of soundmaking taboo, and thus indirectly affected the later development of musical culture in the American colonies. Dancing and theater came to be outlawed in England. Listeners who in Elizabethan times enjoyed minstrels and lovely songs were now exposed to the interminable dreary sermonizing of ministers (30). In southern Europe where Catholicism reigned, a more satisfactory balance between human needs and acoustical practice was achieved. After Dufay (A.D. 1400-1474) the *bass* voice was added to the previous *soprano, alto,* and *tenor,* an arrangement in music which corresponds to the different registers of the voice. Like its poetry, painting, and literature, the music of the Renaissance depicts nature realistically through direct imitation. Songs were written which mimic birds, rhythmically capture the stampeding of horses, and openly project the sighs of lovers and the shouts of warriors (75).

As composers experimented with chromatic progressions, irregular meters, and other acoustic patterns forbidden by Gregorian rules, the emotive potentials in music increased rapidly. Individual styles of soundmaking began to flourish. One of the most dramatic chapters in Renaissance history concerns Gesualdo of Venosa (1560-1613), a nobleman who killed his wife and her lover during a fit of jealous revenge. He was a gifted amateur musician and wrote some of the most heartrending madrigals ever heard (49). Another revealing acoustical practice of this time had to do with the use of sounds for deceiving the authorities. To bring out hidden meanings in texts, certain composers scored pertinent lines of songs with chromatic intervals recognizable only to those in the know. This facilitated the secret communication of contraband ideas in centers of religious controversy such as Amsterdam (74).

A period of introspection, study, and stocktaking followed this crucial historical epoch. For the first time treatises exclusively about sounds were written, for example Daniello Bartoli's book published 1679 in Rome (6). Geminiani, Leopold Mozart, and other famous instrumentalists also produced immensely sophisticated and brilliantly technical commentaries about soundmaking, thus destroying forever a prevalent notion that instrumental musicians are servile and unscholarly persons. Whereas poets, generals, historians, sculptors, and important society figures had been portrayed biographically, no musician was ever so honored before this time. The late seventeenth and early 18th Century witnessed a gradual enrichment of music through harmony, the development of the symphony and the concerto, and the fusion into operatic spectacles of singing, drama, and ballet (100).

Friederich Marpurg (1718-1795), one of the foremost students of soundmaking in the eighteenth century, advanced the development of acoustic aesthetics at this time. He inventoried all of the rhythms, tonal progressions, harmonies, embellishments, and other soundmaking devices which composers had learned to use and which listeners had come to associate with definable mood states and emotional reactions (139). It is of historical interest to review Marpurg's findings, since these represent an important bridge between the acoustics and the psychology of sound. Table I summarizes some of Marpurg's ideas about the acoustic expression of emotion. Similar descriptions of emotional states associated with particular sounds can be found in books written even today about singing, public speaking, and other forms of soundmaking. These descriptions try to directly relate a certain physical acoustic pattern with a supposedly discrete emotional state. For example, Marpurg connects the acoustic pattern "slow melody and dissonance" to an emotional state called "sorrow." At other times he gives no information about the acoustic properties of a sound, but simply defines one emotional state in terms of another, for example "hopefulness is expressed by a proud and exultant melody." Marpurg and his contemporaries also tried to analyze behavioral manifestations which today are

TABLE I

ACOUSTIC EXPRESSION OF EMOTIONAL STATES
According to Friederich Marpurg (139)

Emotion	Expression
Sorrow	Slow, languid melody; sighing; caressing of single words with exquisite tonal material; prevailing dissonant harmony
Happiness	Fast movement; animated and triumphant melody; warm tone color; more consonant harmony
Contentment	A more steady and tranquil melody than with happiness
Repentance	The elements of sorrow, except that a turbulent, lamenting melody is used
Hopefulness	A proud and exultant melody
Fear	Tumbling downward progressions, mainly in the lower register
Laughter	Drawn out, languid tones
Fickleness	Alternating expressions of fear and hope
Timidity	Similar to fear, but often intensified by an expression of impatience
Love	Consonant harmony; soft, flattering melody in broad movements
Hate	Rough harmony and melody
Envy	Growling and annoying tones
Compassion	Soft, smooth, lamenting melody; slow movement; repeated figures in the bass
Jealousy	Introduced by a soft, wavering tone; then an intense, scolding tone; finally a moving and sighing tone; alternating slow and quick movement
Wrath	Expression of hate combined with running notes; frequent sudden changes in the bass; sharp violent movements; shrieking dissonances
Modesty	Wavering, hesitating melody; short, quick stops
Daring	Defiant, rushing melody
Innocence	A pastoral style
Impatience	Rapidly changing, annoying modulations

considered personality attributes rather than emotional characteristics, for instance timidity, modesty, and humility. Thus eighteenth century writers about acoustic aesthetics inadvertently commented not only about emotive soundmaking, but also about the personality patterns and indirectly the social rules that guide the public expression of emotion.

The French and American Revolutions did away with many established social controls and replaced these with new ones. As the speed of life increased, this tempo change reflected itself also in the music of the period, as for example the rugged scherzo of Beethoven (1770-1827)—a form derived from the stately, sedate, and leisurely baroque minuet. Around this time old empires began to collapse, and European states became industrialized. Cannons were made bigger and louder; machines of greater complexity and noisiness were constructed. The population of cities started to mushroom, leading to more crowding, less privacy, and increasing exposure to the sounds of one's neighbors (28). These social conditions undoubtedly affected human auditory reactivity, in particular the toleration for louder sounds.

The nineteenth century was an age of synesthesia. Music, poetry, drama, philosophy, and the visual arts now were deliberately fused by composers—Berlioz, Scriabin, and Wagner—who thought big and believed they could exploit soundmaking to its limit (7). It followed that all sorts of acoustical myths again sprang up: the "ranz des vaches," a tune played on the Alpine horn, was said to be capable of producing suicidal depressions in men of the Swiss guard; Kierkegaard (1813-1855) called music peculiarly abstract; Wagner (1813-1883) used Teutonic tales and stage hocus-pocus to catalyze the supposedly unique powers of acoustic stimuli over men's minds. Darwin (1809-1882) and a few of his followers bravely insisted that soundmaking is a biological activity allied to procreation and the preservation of communal life (24). But their objectivity did not concern musicians until the final collapse of tonality, when Western music for the first time freed itself completely from Gregorian rules (57). The development of twelvetone composition in the West also coincides with the growing recognition of Eastern cultures, languages, and music (83).

Around the time of these historical changes, the sciences of physiology and pathology held increasingly strong attraction for men of medicine, and two individuals who have influenced today's ideas about sound and about behavior lived in this era:

Hermann von Helmholtz (1821-1894), a German physiologist who initiated modern psychoacoustics research (54), and Sigmund Freud (1856-1939), an Austrian neurologist who originated the psychoanalytic investigation of human behavior (44). Helmholtz's theories, transmitted to Freud via his early teachers, made distinct impressions on the first psychoanalytic formulations about mental energy, repression, and unconscious dynamics (12).

Helmholtz concerned himself primarily with the acoustical structure of sounds, with the physiology of auditory reception, and with the way sound energy is transformed by different parts of the ear before the information it encodes is processed by the brain. He was an expert in mathematics, and invented several instruments—including the ophthalmoscope which still is used in medical work—for observing the behavior of the human body. Helmholtz loved music. He was a close friend of the Wagner family in Bayreuth, often attended opera performances and concerts, and played musical instruments (64). He was keenly interested in the relationship between acoustic stimulus patterns and the sense of beauty and pleasure these patterns can engender in listeners. Unlike Freud, Helmholtz was never much inclined to directly observe human emotional reactions by way of the study of psychopathology. He devoted his life mainly to laboratory research, something he rather regretted when, at the close of his magnificent study of sounds, he admits that his investigations had to be stopped "at the point where the more interesting part of musical aesthetics begins, the aim being to explain the wonders of great works of art, and to learn the utterances and actions of the various affections of the mind (54)."

Freud on the other hand intently studied various mental and emotional events in himself and his patients. He was fascinated by dreams, jokes, accidental behavior, psychopathology, even telepathy, and constantly tried to relate these phenomena to unconscious psychic processes (61). Though never directly involved in studies of soundmaking, Freud's great contribution to this field is that he removed—by encouraging free association—many of the inhibitions to soundmaking which his patients felt internally and which crippled their behavior in various ways. One might compare his treatment to the work of an expert music teacher: Freud made regular appointments to see his patients and listened to them at length; he then reflected on what he heard, the appropriateness of the patients' thoughts to their behavior, and the ways in which healthy impulses towards selfexpression had become stunted or diverted to pathologic activity (43). Unlike Helmholtz, Freud seemed not too interested in music; his few comments about this form of soundmaking are found in letters and none in his scientific papers. It has been said that Freud was somewhat superstitious about music's alleged power over the mind. Little is known about his treatment of musicians, for example Gustav Mahler and Bruno Walter, who were Freud's patients, except that this was intensive, brief, and based on a highly intuitive understanding of the patient's problems (136).

To evaluate 20th Century trends in acoustic communication is risky since these are currently evolving and subject to change. Everyone is aware of the many spectacular technologic successes of our time—radio, telephone, the tape-recorder, and artificial satellites—which facilitate signal exchange. But when it comes to the understanding of sounds and the reaching of agreements among soundmakers from different nations, great problems still remain. In 1939, World Fairs both in New York and in San Francisco demonstrated Voders capable of synthesizing recognizable speech sounds; but to date no concord has been achieved as to which set of speech sounds should be made into an international language (98). There is a surprising amount of resistance to new approaches in language—even the writing of new dictionaries (34). This is unfortunate, since fear and intolerance of deviation from standard ways to make sounds may impede communication across national boundaries and could be a terrible handicap if our planet is ever to meet competition from creatures on other stars.

While all of us today must live with the everpresent danger of a massive noise—a thermonuclear blast which threatens to silence all human soundmaking forever—there are also some optimistic advances in acoustic communication. One of these is the growing interest in psychotherapy as a form of soundmaking about human needs and human values (26). Another is the increasingly precise way in which chemical agents can be used to

improve communicative behavior (40). New methods for studying acoustic communication in health and disease are being
developed (123). On the musical scene there is the promising
evolution of entertainment based on tape-recorded sounds. Composition devoid of hidebound rules and outmoded tradition is being practiced, and use is made of noise, nature sounds, and elec-
tronically synthesized acoustic patterns. These innovations indicate a trend toward greater freedom of acoustic expression and
may hopefully increase our general toleration for what may at
first sound strange and unpleasant.

SUMMARY

This chapter shows how trends in soundmaking have changed
throughout history in accordance with man's different views of
nature and changes in his attitudes toward self-expression. Information about acoustic communication in pre-Christian cultures
is presented. The influence of military objectives and of religious
dogma on patterns of soundmaking is discussed. Western musical
aesthetics, particularly that of the eighteenth century, is reviewed
in some detail. Brief mention is made of Helmholtz, the first
psychoacoustician, and of Freud, the first psychoanalyst. Physiologic theories which Helmholtz proposed in connection with his
study of sensory processes had an influence on Freud's early thinking. While a good deal is already known about what psychoneurotic and other patients talk about, the symbolic significance
of how they speak and the meaning of their as yet ill-defined
emotional soundmaking remains a problem for intensive research.
In our own century acoustic communication is enhanced by technical devices which can overcome the delaying effects of distance
and time. But because many different meanings are attributable
to identical sound patterns, there is much still to be done towards
improving the process of acoustic communication across individual and group boundaries. Semantic and linguistic studies focus
on verbal denotative aspects of this problem. The present book
deals primarily with nonverbal soundmaking and how emotions
are communicated acoustically.

Chapter 2

RUDIMENTARY SOUNDS

How human soundmaking began is one of those unanswerable questions that have kept philosophers busy for centuries. Even the best thinkers—for example Plato (102)—fall back on sheer guesswork because no acoustic facts about sounds produced by the first human creatures are available. Cavemen lacked tape-recorders and other means to collect sounds for posterity. Their drawings, pottery, and other visual artefacts tell us little about vocal soundmaking, the most elaborately developed form of acoustic communication among mammals.

ANIMAL SOUNDS

Acoustic studies of animal sounds suggest that human sound-making was by no means suddenly acquired as some special or superior form of communication. Rather, living creatures came gradually to utilize sounds in the course of evolution—particularly the evolution of territorial behavior.

According to Hediger, *sounds which stand for enemy* were the first to become meaningful (53). Acoustic alarm signals are vital for individual and group survival, since such sounds can indicate the presence of danger, warn friends, and frighten predators. Alarm signals have been detected among fish. The splash of a fleeing frog is an alarm signal, even though the animal accidentally produces this sound while escaping. Reptiles hiss and whistle to indicate alarm; and birds produce a variety of danger sounds.

Mating calls are next in a theoretical hierarchy of the important animal sounds. These draw male and female together for procreation. They also chase away possible intruders, and among certain animals are identical with assertions of territorial possession (53). Possibly mating calls also influence the production and circulation of hormones, and more directly affect sexual physiology. McLean has noted exuberant vocal screeching associated with experimentally produced penile erections among squirrel monkeys, but these sounds have not been analyzed acoustically, nor is their function in spontaneous sexual activity known (78).

Signals that associate mother and child represent the third most important animal sound. Some shell-born embryos make noises that indicate readiness to hatch. Baby monkeys hum to elicit coddling. Mothers make sounds to attract and orient their newborn offspring, and probably to stimulate them in eating, locomotion, and other activities.

Social sounds used in larger animal communities to connote departure, return, and other interactions are probably derivatives of the mother-child sounds.

Food sounds probably come closest to what we call words in human speech. Message exchange about food must include information about its whereabouts, nature, and availability. Much of this is probably transmitted non-acoustically, for example with ritualized dances, pointing, and other visual signals.

Which features of animal soundmaking have been incorporated into human communication? According to Hockett, we share ten of the thirteen "design-features" of speech with our pets and zoo-inhabitants (56):

1. *Vocal-auditory channel* — The use of this channel enables the animal to have much of its body free for other activities besides communication.

2. *Broadcast transmission and directional reception* — This makes it possible for a meaningful signal to be heard by any auditory system within earshot, and enables the receiver to localize the soundmaker through binaural detection.

3. *Rapid fading* — This design-feature of speech prevents a signal from lingering. The hearer cannot wait until it seems convenient to receive a message, but must focus his attention on what is said.

4. *Interchangeability* — The speaker is able to reproduce any message that he understands.

5. *Total feedback* — When a speaker hears what he says, this enables him to internalize his communicative behavior, an important step in what is called thinking.

6. *Specialization* — The body movements and spreading of sound waves serve no function other than as signals for communication.

7. *Semanticity* — There are relatively fixed associations between acoustic signals and events or things of the external environment, hence a message composed of acoustic signals can trigger a specific result.

8. *Arbitrariness* — The semantic associations are arbitrarily agreed upon; thus what sound signals can be used to communicate about is unlimited.

9. *Discreteness* — In a given language, the range and variety of useful sound signals is restricted to a relatively small number, and the differences between these few basic sounds is absolute.

10. *Displacement*—Semantic associations can also be made between sound patterns and things that are remote in space and time.

Only three of Hockett's 13 design-features of speech are uniquely human:

11. *Productivity* — This is the capacity to use basic sounds in order to construct new acoustic entities which have never been said or heard before and yet can be understood by the speakers of the language.

12. *Traditional transmission* — Whereas the capacity to acquire a language is inherited, the detailed conventions of any given language are transmitted non-genetically by learning and teaching.

13. *Duality of patterning* — The huge vocabulary of every human language represents the discrete sequential organization of a small stock of basic sounds that in themselves are semantically meaningless.

Certain of the acoustic interactions of animals also resemble *abnormalities* of human speech. For example, crickets make sounds in ways closely resembling what psychiatrists call *echolalia* and *stuttering*. One cricket starts to chirp and a moment later another cricket joins in and also makes noises. Soon the echoing follower synchronizes its chirping with the leader. If the leader is now silenced, the follower will either hesitate or stop also. Silencing the follower rarely causes the leader to stutter (1).

Much of the soundmaking of animals resembles *emotive communication* as it occurs when human beings are excited, depressed, angry, or afraid. For instance, gibbon monkeys produce at least fourteen distinctive vocalizations. According to La Barre, these sounds serve "in spreading information about an individual's state of mind or communicate a generalized emotional tone throughout the band so all members come to have the same attitude towards a situation" (69). The gibbon's 14 sounds include five vocal expressions for states of well-being, four indicating illness or fear, four of an intermediate state, and one for intense excitement.

BABY SOUNDS

The human infant is by definition speechless, yet he communicates volubly with sounds. This suggests a second approach, in our search for rudimentary acoustic patterns. Crying is the most characteristic baby sound, and an analysis of its acoustic properties will concern us in Chapter 4. Less information is available about other sounds which human newborns make. In an unpublished study, Kurtz described eighteen distinctive patterns of acoustic behavior which he observed during the first twenty-four hours in the life of a baby (68).

> *The Cry* — this tonal sound of about one second duration is the most characteristic acoustic emission of the human infant. It has a rise-and-fall pattern capped by a loud peak. (More detailed characteristics of the cry are discussed in Chapter 4.)
>
> *The Scream* — when a baby is extremely excited it screams. This sound is louder than a cry and at its peak becomes noisy instead of remaining tonal.
>
> *The Burp* — this sound accompanies eructation of the air bubble which usually collects in a baby's stomach during feeding.
>
> *The Vomit Sound* — this is a guttural noise associated with vomiting, usually of low pitch and indefinite duration.
>
> *The Gulp* — this is a highpitched tonal sound of very brief duration that accompanies the sudden inhalation which precedes screaming.

The Laa-sound — this is a type of cry which has a steady, non-fluctuating tone and involves tonguing, responsible for its consonantal quality.

The Breath Sound — this is a very soft nontonal noise produced when the baby exhales without vocalizing.

The Sneeze — this is an explosive reflex sound associated with nasal irritation.

The Cough — this is a reflex ejection noise produced by a spasm due to tracheal irritation.

The Hiccup — this is another reflex sound, usually associated with diaphragmatic irritation.

The Gargle — this is a low pitched noise which resembles the creaking of an old door.

The Whine — this is a nasalized cry.

Mutterings — these are brief vocalic sounds of low intensity that are not part of the cry cycle and recur singly, in pairs, or in triplets.

Squeaks — these are very highpitched, whistlelike tones which occur at moments of intense excitement.

Rises — these are short tonal glides of rising pitch that precede cycles of crying and appear to be abortive attempts to cry.

Whimpers — these are whiny mutterings that appear when an infant is exhausted.

The Lip-puckering Sound — this is a very soft smacking noise that appears when an infant wakes up.

Flatulence — this is a dull, explosive thud produced by the anal discharge of gas.

These eighteen sounds are part of the reflexly-organized spontaneous activity of the twenty-four hour newborn. The extent to which learning influences soundmaking at this age is not known. Studies of intra-uterine conditioning of behavior (120) and rare reports of intra-uterine vocalization (95) suggest that even newborns may already have some capacity to organize their soundmaking in terms of environmental cues. Kurtz was quite impressed with the change in soundmaking while the infant was tied down for circumcision and during the operation itself. He recorded some extremely highpitched screeches and falsetto-cries at these times and interpreted the sounds as rudimentary signs of pain. Similar observations about acoustic expressions of discomfort were made by Lewis (72).

Within the first year of life an elaboration of this rudimentary soundmaking takes place, as a consequence both of the baby's physical maturation and the social stimuli to which he is exposed. Some of the resulting sounds are later used for speech, as we shall see shortly. Others do not become linguistic cues, but play a role in the nonverbal acoustic communication of feeling states (91). Included here are these baby sounds:

Sucking — this is a soft highpitched noise of brief duration which recurs in a regular rhythmic pattern. It results from the baby's oral manipulation of his mother's breast, a rubber nipple, or other objects introduced into the mouth.

The Razzberry — this is a continuous noise produced by air forced out through saliva-covered lips or against objects such as toys and spoons introduced into the mouth.

Laughter — this is a tonal explosion that recurs rapidly and rhythmically. Like smiling, it is part of a baby's earliest social response, and can usually be triggered off by familiar visual stimuli, tickling, or pleasant passive (later active) movements of the limbs.

Banging — these are loud friction noises of brief duration that vary acoustically depending on the objects which are banged. Banging results first from rapid thrashing movements of the arms and legs against solid obstacles like the floor or bed, and later is produced with movable objects like toys, bottles, etc.

Humming — this is a soft tone emitted steadily or in a series of discontinuous bursts. It is usually produced with the lips closed, air which has been set into vibration by the larynx being ejected through the nose.

Vocalization — this is a seemingly random form of tonal soundmaking that varies considerably in its acoustic pattern. Vocalization usually occurs with the mouth wide open. It does not have the typically recurrent rhythmicity of laughter or crying.

Lalling — this is vocalization plus articulation by the mid-mouth structures (top of the palate, blade of the tongue, and side of the gums) intermittently interrupting the vocal air-stream. This produces an ambiguous consonantal quality which resembles *laa* or *gaa.*

Babbling — this is another variant of vocalization, similar to lalling except that the air-column is here interrupted more anteriorly, by the front of the mouth (lips, tip of the tongue, front of the gums). The consonantal quality *daa,* *baa,* or *paa* results.

Adults also make baby sounds, usually under conditions of emotional disturbance which will be discussed in later chapters. When this happens their soundmaking, including speech, carries with it distinctly infantile connotations. Probably because of the protective, pejorative, and other strongly emotional responses which these sounds in turn elicit from listeners, society regulates the production of baby sounds or outlaws them entirely. For example, silence is enforced in various ways by different cultures during funerals, in hospitals, and in public gatherings not only to protect people from excessive auditory stimulation (142), but also because the amount of infantile soundmaking is thus reduced and emotional communication is kept under control. Outbursts of baby sounds—banging, applause, laughter, razzberries, etc.—are permitted at intervals to relieve tension, but only under command of a master-of-ceremonies, conductor, orator, or other leader whose function it is, among other things, to regulate soundmaking.

There are also conditions of physiologic stress when adults make baby sounds. In particular burps, vomit sounds, gulps, breath noise, sneezing, coughing, and hiccups occur reflexly throughout life. These sounds are then meaningful acoustic byproducts of protective processes that guard the body against injury, intoxication, or infection (117). Certain baby sounds, for instance sucking and babbling, also occur as the result of brain lesions which apparently impair adult inhibitions against soundmaking (29).

RUDIMENTARY SPEECH SOUNDS

Speech is the form of soundmaking which characterizes verbal behavior. Its acoustic analysis will be taken up in Chapter 5. Here we are concerned with the phonetic ingredients of speech, and in the relationship between speech and baby sound-making.

Crying, humming, vocalizing, and other soundmaking activities observed in the nursery involve similar acoustic mechanisms which later on are used for speaking. Air is pushed out of the lungs and set into vibration by movements of the vocal cords. The resulting sound is shaped by constrictions of the throat and mouth. Resonance of various body parts contributes to the amplitude and wave-form of the final signal (35). But the orderly, sequential emission of meaningful acoustic signals that is speech requires far more social experience and cerebral organization than are available to a child. Even during puberty and adolescence speech is often a compromise between reflexive and verbal patterns of soundmaking. Few persons become effective speakers—in the sense that they can say what they want and need to say, at the time indicated for this, and to the appropriate listeners—before they reach their late twenties or early thirties. Some persons never learn to speak, and in that sense never become adult in their acoustic behavior (3).

Certain baby sounds—for example vocalization, lalling, and babbling—come close to the phonetic soundmaking that in speech comprises vowel and consonant production. At least eight baby sounds which sufficiently resemble speech to be called phonetic have been identified: Irwin and coworkers recognized the sound [æ] as in *a*pple in 90 percent of the sound made by babies during the first few days of life. They also described as "infant speech" the sounds [ɪ] as in *i*ll, [ɛ] as in *e*dible, [ʌ] as in *u*tter, [u] as in b*oo*t, [h] as in *h*at, [l] as in *l*ook, and a glottal stop which resembles the catch between the two syllables of the admonitory "ah ah!" (60).

During the first two and a half years of life as a baby grows bigger, learns to feed itself, and manages to sit up and then walk, the number of baby sounds resembling speech also gradually expands from the original eight towards the quantity required by the particular language spoken in the child's community. Also a change takes place in the child's *method* for producing sounds. Among the American babies studied by Irwin, there was a noticeable shift in the production of consonantal sounds from the back of the mouth to the front: two months after birth 98 percent of the consonantal sounds came from the back of the throat (glottal and velar sounds); by the age of two and one-half years, 77 per cent of the consonants came from the front of the mouth (labial and postdental sounds). In Chapter 10 we shall see that certain severely regressed psychiatric patients produce predominantly back consonants and, like infants, rarely articulate with the front of the mouth.

While it seems that learning to speak requires that a growing child add new sounds to his original repertoire of eight speech-like baby sounds, actually it is just as important that he stop making many of the twenty-six sounds used in the nursery. Correct speech involves volitional control so that reflexive sound-making like crying, vomiting, and lip-puckering is held back. The growing child must also learn to inhibit those baby sounds like sucking and laughter which connote infantile behavior, communicate emotionality, and are only permissible among adults under limited social conditions.

Speech is the careful, orderly, regulated emission of a limited number of structurally significant sounds called *phonemes*. These are about .06 second in duration under average conditions of speaking. Like chemical elements, isolated phonemes are hard to find except in laboratories; actual speaking requires that phonemes be combined into nuclear semantic clusters called *morphemes*. These sounds take up roughly 0.2 second, depending on how fast one speaks. Morphemes are the minimal bearers of information in the cognitive sense; they are semantic symbols which are useful for communication because speakers agree on what the individual sounds stand for (18).

Let us play with a few rudimentary speech sounds to see what they can do. Take for instance the word *cat;* it is composed of three phonemes, /k/, /æ/, and /t/,* none of which independently have any meaning. But strung together, these meaningless sounds turn into /kæt/, a sound which refers by agreement to a small, four-footed animal that meows. We can hook additional sounds to this morpheme to change its meaning. For example, by adding the phoneme /l/ to our /kæt/ we make it into /kætl/, a sound that refers to large four-footed animals which

---

* By linguistic convention, phonetic notation is enclosed in brackets [ ], while phonemic signs are indicated by slashes / /.

moo and produce milk and steaks. Finally, we can string several morphemes and phonemes together into a chain and come up with a polysyllabic word that still contains our /kæt/ but has nothing to do with cats. Here is one: /kætəpilər/, the sound for a furry, crawling worm, the word *caterpillar*.

One can readily see from the examples cited above that direct relationships do not necessarily exist between the acoustic and the referential properties of words. In fact, it so happened that our short unappetizing animal, the caterpillar, carries an acoustic label a good deal longer and intricate than cattle, the word for large useful beasts. Furthermore, when a caterpillar grows up it changes into a butterfly—really a most arbitrary metamorphosis if you look at it phonetically! This is why linguists are so interested in history and psychology; to understand acoustic communication, one must explore seemingly arbitrary sound-meaning combinations and how these arose through repeated usage (15).

When a speech sound acoustically imitates what it stands for, this process of symbolization is called *onomatopoeia*. For example, the words *bang, hiss,* and *clap* mimic the very noises they refer to. Onomatopoeic soundmaking resembles pointing; it is a direct way to indicate what you mean and does not require cumbersome vocabulary rules (135). Listening is more important than thinking when it comes to the interpretation of onomatopoeic sounds. This is why children love onomatopoeic rhymes, songs, and word-games—the pleasure, acoustics, and referential properties of this rudimentary speech form are all wrapped up in the sound of the words (85). Poets use onomatopoeias when their aim is to create an attractive sound pattern rather than to focus on the meaning of words.

Onomatopoeic speech also occurs when the thinking processes are strongly driven by emotions. For example, a patient, a fearful young man who had exhausted himself in unusually vigorous sexual activity over a sunny weekend, became obsessed with the word *tangential*. At the time this word had no logical connotation for him, but by associating to its sound he was led to think of "tanned genitals." Apparently this idea lost its strongly emotional flavor once the component words were fused and onomatopoeically expressed by the neutral word "tangential." Similarly, impolite ideas may lose some of their emotional charge when expressed by means of "four-letter" words. *Piss, shit,* and *fuck,* for example, have little meaning but onomatopoeically have something of the aggressive, sexual, and tabood quality of the acts referred to.

Other speech devices for the communication of feelings depend on the structure of the language code used (122). For instance, in English a common way to belittle a person is to slice a few phonemes from his name—Thomas→Tom, Margaret→Mag, Jonathan→John. One can further demote the person by then sticking an *ee* sound onto the raw end of the name—Tommy, Maggy, Johnny. Code-switching is another speech trick used to disconnect words from their formal semantic meaning and to increase emotional communication. One can do this by using archaic words, nonsense sounds, technical jargon, baby-talk, or a foreign accent.

Finally, it is possible to increase or decrease the emotional range of speech by selectively manipulating its rhythm, intensity, pitch, tone, speed, shape, and orderliness. This will be discussed more extensively in later chapters.

SUMMARY

To understand acoustic communication of emotion, we must review the more primitive soundmaking patterns produced by animals and by human infants. This chapter mentions some of Hediger's recent observations about animal signals. It then summarizes the thirteen "design-features" of speech that Hockett has proposed to explain similarities and differences between human and nonhuman soundmaking. The baby's early preverbal soundmaking, and how this is later integrated into adult speech, are discussed. It appears that only well-differentiated, healthy, adult human beings possess the skill for using verbal sounds in the precise way necessary to denote and abstract about the environment. Abnormalities in this aspect of communication are often taken to indicate developmental immaturity or psychopathology. While some acoustic patterns among animals resemble abnormal human soundmaking, even the most deteriorated speech of a mentally defective person seems to be more complex than any language system yet devised by animals.

Chapter 3

HOW TO MAKE STATEMENTS
ABOUT SOUND

Before we go any further into the analysis of soundmaking, it is necessary to consider the problem of descriptive terminology. Words like pitch, loudness, and rhythm already appeared in the previous chapters. Now these and other terms must be defined. This chapter also introduces an acoustic method for measuring sounds, which is applied for the clinical studies to be reported subsequently.

Sounds are vibratory occurrences which listeners perceive auditorily and integrate into mental patterns based also on information from nonacoustic sources like visual input, memory, fantasy, and feeling states (63). Many of the complex psychophysiologic processes involved take place outside the listener's awareness. That part of the auditory pattern which a listener does notice must be translated into words if it is to be communicated to others. Since this translation itself comprises the complicated chain of phonetic and semantic events outlined in Chapter 2, it is not surprising that statements made about sounds often have little to do with actual acoustical happenings. At best the verbal statements one can make about sounds reveal a small portion of this total acoustic-auditory pattern (128).

To serve practical needs, those persons who study acoustic phenomena and teach soundmaking have devised various terminologies and descriptive schemes for communicating verbally about sounds. Musicians speak of intonation, timbre, and tempo; acousticians talk of noise, decibels, and frequencies; linguists use terms like inflection, stress, and pitch levels; voice therapists describe hoarseness, registers, and melody. This is but a small sample from some of the many different and often confusing terms used to describe sounds (5). Future investigations will have to find out which words from the various disciplines actually refer to identical acoustic phenomena. At the present time all one can do is try to eliminate the redundancy of overlapping terminologies now in use, and distinguish between *qualitative attributes, visualization of sound,* and *acoustic measurement.*

QUALITATIVE ATTRIBUTES OF SOUND

Qualitative attributes are functions of the system *sound-plus-listener.* They derive from the admixture of sensory and interpretive responses listeners display towards the sound in question. Qualitative attributes fall into seven categories, each of which represents a gradient confined by extreme endpoints. The categories are:

1. rhythmicity
2. intensity
3. pitch
4. tone
5. speed
6. shape
7. orderliness

1. *Rhythmicity* refers to those characteristics of sound defined along the gradient

rhythmic ————————— *irregular*

An example of a rhythmic sound is one produced by someone rocking back and forth in a rocking chair; the temporal pattern of this sound is regular and predictably recurrent. At the other extreme is the sound produced when someone leans back slowly in a squeaky swivel chair. This sound has little predictable timing.

Rhythmicity is one of the most basic attributes of sounds living creatures produce. There is evidence for an innate biologic rhythmicity (22) and for spontaneous fetal rhythmicity among mammals enhanced by throbbing of the maternal uterus (80). The regular ticking of a clock or metronome is rhythmic, in contrast to the roaring of an electronic white-noise generator or the sound of a waterfall.

2. *Intensity* refers to the characteristics of sound as defined along the gradient

loud ——————— *soft*

The level at which sound produces pain in addition to auditory sensation (about 120 decibels) is a useful end-point for loudness. The physiologic threshold of hearing (0 decibels) represents the soft extreme of this gradient (10).

Few sounds of human origin ever reach the pain threshold. Jet-engine noise, artillery blasts, and other high-intensity noises do get this loud, and ear protection is therefore necessary for those in close proximity to the sound source (51). As we shall see in Chapter 4, the peak of a baby's cry also approaches the pain threshold, but only if one measures this sound very close to the infant's mouth. As for extremely soft sounds, there is considerable debate about this, and recent psychoacoustic studies challenge the idea of an absolute physiologic threshold of hearing. Intensity limits of the auditory system seem to vary with age, attentiveness, and the listener's knowledge about a particular stimulus (131). It seems doubtful that absolute silence is attainable. Acoustic vibrations capable of moving the eardrum only a fraction the diameter of one hydrogen atom suffice to produce some sensation. Also the ear mechanism itself produces a certain amount of noise (Weaver-Bray Effect).

3. *Pitch* refers to the characteristics of sound as defined along the gradient

high-pitched ——————— *low-pitched*

Pitch depends on the frequency of acoustic vibrations reaching the ear. Endpoints for the pitch gradient are difficult to define, since in making pitch judgements, listeners are also influenced by other attributes of the acoustic stimulus than pitch (73). Nevertheless, most textbooks give the audible frequency range of hearing as 20,000 cycles per second for the high end, and 20 cycles per second for the low end. Age is an important consideration here, since children have a greater hearing range than do older people.

The hissing noise of certain consonants (s, ch, z, f, th) can get up to 10,000 cps or to even higher frequencies (see Chapter 5). But musical sensibility on which pitch judgement is based seems to stop around 4,000 cps, approximately the pitch of the highest note on the piano, C=4,186 cps. Very low-pitched sounds are perceived in more than just an auditory sense; they may be felt as rumbling, as vibrations, or environmental turbulence, as for example the extremely low tones of a pipe organ. Pitch perception becomes hazy at these low frequencies; the lowest A of the piano vibrates at 27.5 cps.

4. *Tone* refers to the characteristics of sound as defined along the gradient

tonal ————————— noisy

A tonal sound is made up of a single vibratory frequency or contains several vibratory frequencies which are simple multiples of each other. At the opposite extreme is noise (not to be confused with noise in the sense of "unwanted sound"). Noise is composed of numerous vibratory frequencies that overlap and intermingle with one another to produce highly complex wave-forms (11).

At the tonal end of this gradient is the socalled "pure tone"; it represents a sine-wave pattern of uniform acoustic vibration at a single point of the frequency spectrum. For instance, a tuning fork gently set into motion produces a pure tone. The opposite extreme, random wave forms called noise, is exemplified by the output of a white-noise generator. This electronic device produces acoustic vibrations simultaneously along the entire audible frequency spectrum from 20 to 20,000 cps.

5. *Speed* refers to the characteristics of sound as defined along the gradient

fast ————————— slow

Our ability to perceive the speed of acoustic stimuli is, as in the case of intensity, pitch, and tone, governed by the physiologic limitations of the hearing apparatus. At fast speeds, successive acoustic impulses merge together, producing the sensation of a steady sound. This happens when the impulse rate begins to exceed twenty sounds per second. At the slow end of the gradient there is a lapse of consciousness after about 0.8 second, so that when impulses fall below the rate of one sound per second the listener needs additional acoustic cues—say a melody or meaningful context—to sustain his attention to the sound (10).

Flutists, clarinetists, and other players of woodwind instruments may approach the fast limits of sound by "triple-tonguing" their instruments; virtuoso violinists and pianists often trill quickly enough to produce a blur of sounds. But in speech where a high degree of comprehensibility is desired, speed is held down to an optimal level of about five morphemes per second, with frequent interruptions of soundmaking to give the listener time to catch on. The resting cardiac pulse, and the lethargic march of a funeral procession exemplify slow forms of soundmaking. Below that rate, it takes a composer of Beethoven's skill to sustain the impression of speed; some of his *largo* movements are played as slowly as forty impulses per minute.

6. *Shape* refers to the characteristics of sound as defined along the gradient

impulsive —————— *reverberant*

The explosive sound of a pistol shot in an anechoic chamber exemplifies a sound at the impulsive end of the gradient. It begins suddenly, rises rapidly to a peak intensity, and decays quickly to silence. This kind of sound is experienced subjectively as abrupt and crashing. At the reverberant extreme is sound like that of water running continuously into a large empty barrel. This sound starts gradually, builds into a steadily reverberating pattern which maintains a semi-tonal quality depending on the force of the water and the shape of the barrel, and dies out very slowly.

Shape as used here refers to the acoustic elements comprised by the technical term *envelope* (84). It is an attribute related to the onset, growth, steady-state, duration, decay, and termination of an individual sound. A listener's perception of shape depends not only on the wave-form at its point of origin, but also on the distance of the listener from this point and the acoustic properties of the surrounding room.

7. *Orderliness* refers to the characteristics of sound as defined along the gradient

compact ————————— expanded

A sound is compact when its single units are approximated into an orderly recognizable pattern. This approximation may be basically rhythmic as in the Morse code, tonal as in the chiming of Big Ben, or simultaneously rhythmic and tonal as in a musical melody. Compactness can also be a function of patterned intensity, as for instance the stress accents in poetry. Certain contemporary music which serially specifies intensity gradations also gains compactness thereby. At the expanded extreme of the gradient, sounds lack rhythm, tone, or intensity organization and are called dissonant, monotonous, or cacophonic.

In contrast to rhythmicity which appears to be a biologically determined auditory experience, orderliness depends greatly on the listener's social adaptation and learn-

[a]	*alms*	[amz]	[i]	*pin*	[pin]	[r]	*rod*	[rɑd]
[ɑ]	*odd*	[ɑd]	[j]	*yes*	[jes]	[s]	*sod*	[sɑd]
[b]	*big*	[big]	[ǰ]	*gem*	[ǰem]	[š]	*shove*	[šov]
[č]	*chin*	[čin]	[k]	*cat* ·	[kɛt]	[t]	*tin*	[tin]
[d]	*dig*	[dig]	[l]	*lamb*	[lɛm]	[θ]	*thin*	[θin]
[ð]	*then*	[ðen]	[m]	*miss*	[mis]	[u]	*put*	[put]
[e]	*egg*	[eg]	[n]	*knot*	[nɑt]	[v]	*van*	[vɛn]
[ɛ]	*add*	[ɛd]	[ŋ]	*sing*	[siŋ]	[w]	*wag*	[wɛg]
[f]	*fan*	[fɛn]	[o]	*up*	[op]	[z]	*zip*	[zip]
[g]	*give*	[giv]	[ɔ]	*ought*	[ɔt]	[ž]	*rouge*	[ruwž]
[h]	*hand*	[hɛnd]	[p]	*pin*	[pin]			

Fig. 1. A phonetic alphabet of standard English (from p. 91, Bloomfield, L. : *Language*, Henry Holt and Co., New York, 1933 (c) 1961).

ing. For example, before one learns to recognize the orderliness of a foreign language it sounds chaotic and incomprehensible. Also much music criticism represents a prejudice against those acoustic patterns which appear expanded, i. e., sounds whose orderliness escapes the listener.

VISUALIZATION OF SOUNDS

Visualization stands half-way between verbal description and acoustic measurement as a way to make statements about sound. The first successful visualization of human sounds was probably the *phonetic alphabet,* of ancient Egyptian origins. A phonetic alphabet consists of schematized pictures of individual speech sounds, often in terms of their anatomic origins (see Fig. 1). For example, in our alphabet "O" portrays the mouth open and rounded for production of this vowel; the letter "B" portrays the lips compressed as during articulation of this consonant. A phonetic alphabet distorts the flowing nature of soundmaking so as to visualize small informational segments. It artificially stops sound in midstream, as it were, much like a single motionpicture frame, which freezes the continuous character of bodily movement.

The *system of neumes* visualizes sound in a more natural way; added to the phonetic alphabet it shows how the voice is inflected during speech (See Figure 2). Neumes were invented in ancient times to denote vocal embellishment for the chanting of prayers (41): the hand was raised to indicate a rise in pitch, lowered to indicated a fall in pitch, and shaken back and forth to indicate wavering tones. The vigor of these hand movements indicated various degrees of intensity. These hand signals were later translated into written signs and incorporated into texts, for example the Hebrew Bible. Ultimately neumes came into prominence throughout the world; they are found in the Gagaku Plays of Japan, Roman Catholic Hymnals, and Folk Song Books of the Middle East. The diacritical marks in dictionaries, the accentual notation used to mark poetic meter, and some of the signs used in modern microlinguistics are all descendants of the old system of neumes. These visual signs improve the accuracy of our phonetic alphabet.

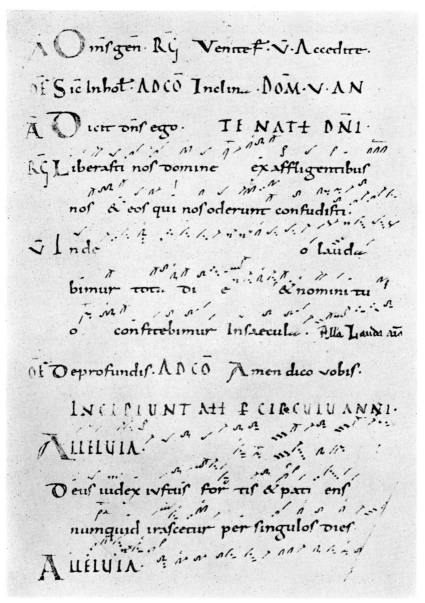

Fig. 2. Neume notation from the St. Gall Cantatorium (late 9th Century).

Neumes have the defect of showing pitch only in relative terms. Placing the signs on a horizontal grid of defined pitch levels increases their accuracy. This is the essence of *musical notation,* an invention of Guido d'Arezzo (11th Century AD). Modern notation uses five lines to indicate pitch; different clefs fix the pitch levels absolutely in terms of vibrations per second (96). For example, the soprano clef locates the pitch $G = 384$ cycles per second on the second horizontal line from the bottom of the staff. Dots on and between lines stand for sounds of different pitch. Further accuracy in the notation is achieved by giving time values to these dots, using size, shape, and attached brackets as differentiating cues. While primarily used prescriptively, music has also been successfully employed as a means for describing human sounds. William Gardiner thus visualized animal sounds, human speech and songs, and various other "sounds of nature" (see Fig. 3) in a very interesting book published over a hundred years ago (46).

None of the visualization methods mentioned so far are capable of portraying the intensity and tone characteristics of sound. To do this, *acoustical instruments* are necessary. An optical way for determining the strength of sound waves was developed in 1820 in France, and in 1882 Lord Rayleigh built the first practical precision instrument for measurement of acoustic intensity. These were the beginnings of scientific acoustics as we know it today. At the present time several good devices for making pictures of acoustic events are available. The *oscilloscope* pictures sounds in two dimensions by means of a cathode-ray tube. This easily shows the sine-wave pattern of pure tones. In the case of jagged, complex waveform patterns of more noisy sounds, an oscillogram is more difficult to interpret.

The *sound spectrograph* is an acoustical device that converts sound energy into spots of varying darkness on paper (see Fig. 4). This is done by means of fixed band-pass filters, to be discussed shortly. The entire intensity-frequency-time pattern of sounds up to 2.4 seconds duration can be automatically visualized with this instrument, which has been of great help in acoustic phonetics (103). Cross-sectional studies resembling the intensity-frequency curves shown in Chapters 4 and 5 can also be made.

BIRDS & ANIMALS.

Fig. 3 Musical notation of bird calls, animal sounds, and a child's cry (from p. 258, Gardiner, W. : *The Music of Nature,* Wilkins and Carter, Boston, 1838).

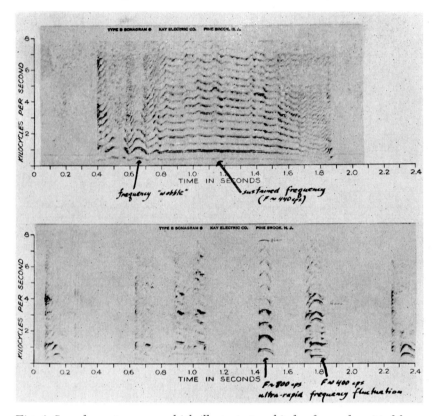

Fig. 4. Sound spectrograms which illustrate two kinds of sound emitted by a newborn baby. Above: *a whine*, characterized by wobbling frequencies (from 0.4 to 0.8 seconds) followed by a sustained tonal pattern with the fundamental around 440 cps. Below: *a squeak*, characterized by ultra-rapid fluctuations in the frequency pattern between 1.4 and 1.8 seconds. The fundamental tone drops from 800 cps to 400 cps within this brief period of time.

ACOUSTIC MEASUREMENT

Acoustic measurement is scientifically the most objective way to make statements about sounds. By means of filters, the sound is separated into its frequency components, much as chemical filtration separates chemical ingredients of differing densities. Depending on the fineness of an acoustic filter, one can study differently-sized spectrum bands in terms of their energy levels

(113). Adjustable band-pass filters measure sound energy at points anywhere along the frequency spectrum. Fixed band-pass filters divide the spectrum into bands of equal size (e.g., octaves, half-octaves, third-octaves, etc.) from one end of the spectrum (20 cps) to the other (20,000 cps). The amount of energy passed by each filter can be visualized, as with the sound spectrograph, or measured with a meter. Acoustic energy levels are directly related to the intensity of sound, as expressed in *decibels*. The decibel is a unit which denotes the ratio between two energy measurements, one of which is equivalent to sound pressure of 0.0002 microbar (0 decibels). Decibels are logarithms and therefore cannot be dealt with by ordinary addition and subtraction as can non-logarithmic units like inches or liters.

While psychiatrists have been tape-recording the sounds of patients for over ten years (17), hardly any have subjected these tapes to acoustic measurement. This is understandable if one considers some of the technical problems involved in an acoustic study of emotionally disturbed persons. Unless a soundproofed, echofree room is used, the recording microphone must be placed close to the patient's mouth. This may be annoying to the patient or the doctor and can interfere with the primary psychotherapeutic task (107). Chapter 7 of this book presents an example of such a situation—a patient who perceived the tape-recording procedure in terms of a dangerous threat to his survival. Also, recording equipment of high quality must be used, and this equipment has to be calibrated in an acoustics laboratory if it is to serve for measurement. Computation of the results can be arduous and the clinician who undertakes acoustic measurement of sounds produced by his patients had better be prepared to devote considerable time to this and to seek professional assistance from qualified acoustical scientists until he becomes familiar with the procedure.

Acoustical science is developing rapidly, and it is entirely possible that by the time you read this book other and better methods for measuring human sounds will have been worked out. The purpose of the method presented here is to specify by acoustic measurement two of the seven qualitative attributes of patient's sounds: *intensity* and *pitch*. Intensity, as you will recall is measured in terms of decibels re 0.0002 microbar; pitch is defined in terms of frequency, or cycles per second.*

The following equipment is used—see Figure 5.

Microphone — Electrovoice 655C, omnidirectional
Tape recorder — Ampex 601, speed 7½ inches per second
Sound Analyzer — H. H. Scott 420A

Fig. 5. Acoustic measurement: A subject is being interviewed. The H. H. Scott Sound Analyzer used for studies reported in this book is shown to the right of the tape-recorder.

This acoustic system is calibrated with Massa 126 and Bruel and Kjaer 4131 microphones as laboratory standards. Best results are obtained when the microphone is in horizontal position, with the sensitive tip ten inches from the patient's mouth. A tall microphone stand, several gooseneck extensions, or a suspension arrangement can be used; the main thing is to have a standard distance between the mouth and the microphone.†

---

* In Europe, the Hertz (Hz) is often used to stand for cycles per second (cps).

† If a unidirectional instead of an omnidirectional microphone is used, special care becomes necessary to assure that the patient speak directly into the microphone instead of focussing his sounds elsewhere, which could falsify measurements.

The volume-setting of the tape recorder is adjusted at the beginning of each recording session so as to obtain a level that does not push the machine beyond its limits and yet picks up soft sounds. The Ampex tape-recorder contains a decibel meter which shows this level, and once an optimal level is selected, it should not be changed, until completion of the recording.

At the end of the recording session, a known sound is placed on each tape containing samples to be measured. This *calibration sound* serves as an objective reference point for the acoustic analysis, just like a known color provides the standard reference in chemical colorimetry. It is customary to calibrate with a 1,000 cps tone at 2 volts from an electronic oscillator, for example, a transistor oscillator manufactured by General Radio Company, Type 1307-A. A ten-decibel step-attenuator is used to reduce the intensity of the calibration sound when samples of low intensity are being studied. For example 60 decibels attenuation gives a calibration sound appropriate for the measurement of softly-speaking depressed patients. With more excited patients, or when studying screams, cries, and other sounds of high intensity, attenuation by 30 or 40 decibels is usually adequate to give the proper 1,000 cps reference tone.

Intensity measurements are read directly from the decibel meter of the sound analyzer. These must be corrected according to the acoustic properties of the microphone and tape-recorder, and by reference to the 1,000 cps calibration tone. Results are then plotted on prepared graph-paper obtained from the Codex Book Company, Norwood, Massachusetts. Octave band measurements are plotted on paper No. 31,460; half-octave band measurements are plotted on paper No. 31,461. The manufacturer prints cut-off points for each band filter on the graph-paper, so only intensity levels need be written in.[*]

SUMMARY

Before we try to analyze human soundmaking in greater detail, it will be necessary to learn how statements are made about sounds. This chapter describes several ways to do this. Descrip-

---

[*] The Bruel-Kjaer third-octave band analyzer, also used in much acoustic work today and applicable to the study of human sounds, denotes intensity levels directly on graph-paper supplied with the machine.

tive methods are the most popular and easiest way to talk about sounds, but words cannot accurately portray all of the dimensions of an acoustic stimulus pattern. I think that seven qualitative attributes are useful in the verbal description of sounds, and some of the terms discussed in this chapter will be applied later in the book. A more scientific approach to sounds is their measurement. A method to be subsequently used in the clinical and experimental study of emotive sounds is outlined here. Some ways for denoting acoustic patterns visually by means of the phonetic alphabet, neumes, musical notation, and the sound spectrograph are also mentioned here.

Chapter 4

THE BABY CRY

It is appropriate to start the acoustic study of human sounds with an analysis of the baby cry. The cry is an arresting sound—part of every person's inborn equipment for obtaining attention. Gardiner, one of the first scientific investigators of human sound-making, observed many interesting cries (46). Engineers have built certain characteristics of crying into machines that call for urgent attention: sirens of fire-trucks, police cars, and ambulances make tonal glides much like babies, and the telephone bell has approximately the cry's rhythm, speed, and orderliness.

My investigation of baby cries began empirically. I tape-recorded a few infants in the hospital nursery and played back the recordings in a thin-walled temporary building where my office was then located. Secretaries busy in other rooms often would drop their work and come running. They had to know what was wrong "with the baby," and some of them spontaneously made comments like "oh, the poor thing must be hungry," "why don't you call it's mother and make sure the baby gets fed," or in one case, "damn that brat, I wish the mother would come and get it out of here before I slash its throat." Something about the baby cry evidently makes this sound easily heard, compels women to come and see what goes on, and evokes various emotional reactions like concern, protectiveness, and hostility.

DESCRIPTIVE AND SPECTROGRAPHIC STUDIES

Some acoustic properties of baby cries were correctly identified in the early descriptive studies of soundmaking. Gardiner, for example, located the pitch of the cry musically, as a descending pitch glide from C (523 cps) to A (440 cps). Spectrographic studies within the past decade have revealed finer acoustic details: Lynip noted that within the first twenty-four hours of life, irregular, long, quavering sounds characteristic of the birth cry change to "rhythmic crying, less intense than at first. The reso-

39

nance became more pronounced. The pitch fundamental rose and at time of intense crying, the voice would break from a low fundamental to a tone of double and quadruple the original pitch" (77). Winitz has been interested in tracing the relationship between crying and speech formation. He used the sound spectrograph and found that babies between nine and fifteen months of age emit an [æ] sound whose first formant is usually located at 575 cps, or one octave higher at 1,000 cps (141). These findings provide some important insights into the acoustic properties of alarm sounds which will be discussed in Chapters 7 and 8.

To get more information about baby cries I set up a tape-recorder in the hospital nursery at 7:00 a.m., a time when infants start to squirm restlessly in their cribs, wake up, and emit the hunger cry—that acoustic signal so well known to parents the world over. The crying babies were carried into an examining room one at a time and recorded by means of a microphone placed 10 inches in front of the mouth. Each baby was recorded for about fifteen minutes and the cries of twelve babies were thus collected.

This is what a typical cry sounds like: it begins suddenly, often with a glottal attack followed by a vowel sound resembling the phoneme /ə/ (as in *a*bout). The pitch level is close to the note A above middle C on the piano (440 cps); same as the open A string on a violin or viola, and also the note that the oboe plays when an orchestra tunes up. The cry starts to change almost immediately: its pitch goes up and the vowel quality changes to /æ/ (as in h*a*t). The cry then reaches a peak at which it is very loud and high-pitched. At that point it may suddenly break into a noisy rasp, called screaming. Or the tonal quality may persist, in which case the sound remains quite properly a cry. After the peak there is a downward glide of pitch to the original pre-peak level. Some cries fall to a slightly lower pitch-level at the end. Occasionally the vowel sound at termination of a cry also changes, into something resembling /e/ (as in *e*dible).

OCTAVE BAND MEASUREMENTS

To measure the sound of baby cries, I applied the acoustic method outlined in Chapter 3. Energy-level readings in adjacent octave bands were taken at the peaks of cries. Figure 6 shows the results of analyzing three typical cries in this way; the graph will be discussed in some detail in order to introduce you to the interpretation of acoustic measurements.

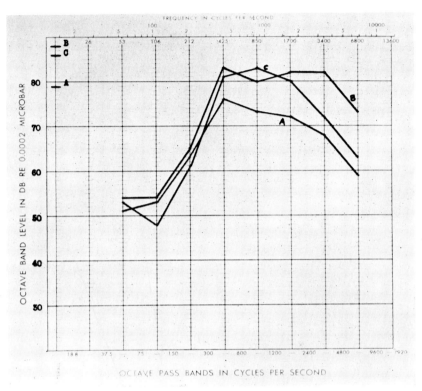

Fig. 6. Acoustic analysis in octave bands of three baby cries
    A—a 72-hours old female, physically very active.
    B—a 72-hours old female, physically inactive, often asleep.
    C—a 48-hours old female, physically inactive, but alert.

Orient yourself in Figure 6 by looking for the horizontal lines which stand for intensity levels (in decibels) and then find the vertical lines which stand for center frequencies of the adjacent octave bands. For example, 53 cps centers the octave band which contains acoustic energy between 37.5 cps and 75 cps. It is best to read the graph from left to right, like a line of print; you will thereby climb upwards along the frequency spectrum from the low end (18.8 cps) to the high end (19,200 cps) of the scale. The plot does not begin before you reach the octave band centered at 53 cps because babies emit practically no low-frequency sound. What the figure shows here is mainly room noise which has been picked up by the recording microphone. Acoustic energy registered in the octave band centered at 106 cps also consists primarily of nonbaby room noise.*

The octave band centered at 212 cps shows an intensity level averaging 63 decibels; this is the first band containing sound produced by the babies. The next octave band, centered at 425 cps, shows even more baby sound. In the case of infant B, the intensity level is now 83 decibels—about as high as it will go for this baby. Intensity levels remain elevated for the next two or three octave bands, and then toward the right-hand side of the curve begin to fall off. The band centered at 6,800 cps is the last octave to carry enough acoustic energy from the baby cries for accurate measurement.

Please remember: the figure you have just looked at does *not* contain information about temporal aspects of the cries— their onset, growth, duration, decay, rhythm, and speed have been ignored. A first look at plots of acoustic measurements may be confusing if one habitually considers a left-to-right sequence to denote time, as in reading Western music and words, sound spectrograms, or operant conditioning curves.

Let us now inspect individually the cries shown in Figure 6 which came from three different babies. Curves A and B represent the cries of two female infants seventy-two hours after birth. Both have a peak at 425 cps, which centers the octave band 300-600 cps. This band includes the frequency 440 cps; we already know this from descriptive studies to be the fundamental tone of the cry. There are individual differences in the heights of the curves: for instance at 425 cps, B is seven decibels above A; at 3,400 cps B is 14 decibels higher than A. These differences indi-

---

* Noise artefacts are generally found on tape-recordings made in hospitals, even when the examining room is lined with acoustic tiles and the environment seems reasonably quiet. This is due to low-frequency energy produced by ventilators, plumbing, and other equipment whose sound is ordinarily excluded from consciousness (51).

cate that infant B put considerably more acoustic energy into its cry than did infant A. Furthermore, infant A's cry shows a gradual decline of acoustic energy above 425 cps, while infant B's cry maintains a high level at 1,700 cps and 3,400 cps. This means that the two cries differ also in the amount of resonance energy, an acoustic term referring to the oomph given to the fundamental tone by its harmonic overtones.

Does the acoustic intensity of a cry correlate with the intensity of the baby's activity during crying? Not necessarily: infant A—the girl who produced the less intense sound denoted by curve A in Figure 6— was an extremely active baby, kicking, contorting her face, and showing generally a great deal of motor activity associated with soundmaking. Baby B, who produced the louder cry, lay quietly in her crib, dozed peacefully between crying bouts, and showed generally little motor excitement during the recording session. Age also does not necessarily correlate directly with soundmaking intensity: the cry of infant C—a baby girl forty-eight hours old—reaches an overall total of 86 decibels (denoted by the horizontal mark at the left of the graph). This is seven decibels higher than the overall intensity attained by A— the physically active seventy-two hours old girl.

Note also the way Baby C distributes the energy of its cry across the frequency spectrum as compared with the other two infants: Curve C comes to a symmetrical-looking hump in the octave band centered by 850 cps, while curve A has a more lopsided appearance and curve B has two humps, one at 425 cps and the other between 1,700 cps and 3,400 cps. These differences in the results of acoustic measurement go along with the varying auditory impressions created by baby cries. In other words, newborn babies differ not only in terms of their weight and appearance, but also produce individually characteristic sound, a matter to be further discussed shortly, when we consider the genetics of baby cries.

HALF-OCTAVE BAND MEASUREMENTS

The octave band analysis of three baby cries just presented resembles a low-power microscopic study which gives a clear picture of gross outlines and patterns but cannot reveal as much detail as does a high-power lens. To achieve a higher degree of resolution in acoustic studies, one uses increasingly narrow band-pass filters. So let us go back to our baby cry specimens, and this time measure these with a sound analyzer set for half-octaves, giving twice the resolution of octave band measurements.

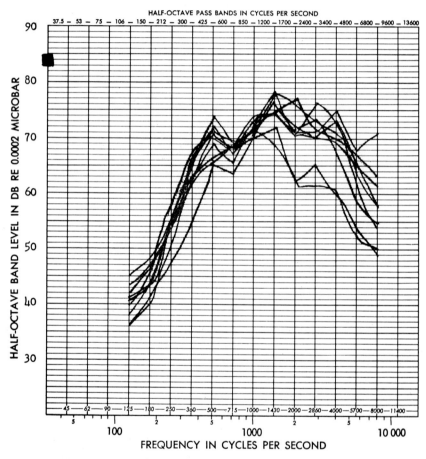

Fig. 7. Acoustic analysis in half-octave bands of nine baby cries.

Figure 7 shows the analysis of nine normal baby cries. In these half-octave band measurements the fundamental tone shows up as a sharply-defined peak at 500 cps, the center frequency of the 425 to 600 cps band. To the left of this peak the curves drop steeply, indicating—as did octave band studies—that babies put out relatively little sound below 425 cps. To the right of the 500 cps peak is a series of peaks and valleys. These jagged portions of the curves indicate the resonance pattern which, though it varies from cry to cry, also displays certain consistencies. For example, the highest intensity level reached by any of the curves is at 1,430 cps, the center frequency of the 1,200 to 1,700 cps band. Prominent peaks of acoustic energy are also found at 2,000 cps, 2,860 cps, and 4,000 cps.

Overall intensity levels of the nine baby cries shown here range from 83 to 85 decibels, as indicated at the left-hand margin of the graph. This narrow range in the intensity of infantile soundmaking suggests that babies who are abnormal in other respects may also deviate in the acoustic characteristics of their cries. This hypothesis has been partially confirmed by Dr. Karelitz, a pediatrician in New York, who has compared the acoustic outputs of mongoloid and other neurologically abnormal babies to the cries of normal infants (62).

TABLE II

NOISE LEVELS FOR VARIOUS SOURCES AND LOCATIONS (84)

Source or Description of Noise		Noise Level in Decibels
Hammer Blows on Steel Plate	2 ft.	114
Riveter	35 ft.	97
Factory		78
Busy Street Traffic		68
Large Office		65
Ordinary Conversation	3 ft.	65
Large Store		63
Factory Office		63
Medium Store		62
Restaurant		60
Residential Street		58
Medium Office		58
Garage		55
Small Store		52
Theatre		42
Hotel		42
Apartment		42
House, Large City		40
House, Country		30
Average Whisper	4 ft.	20
Quiet Whisper	5 ft.	10
Rustle of Leaves in Gentle Breeze		10

An acoustic output in excess of 80 decibels is really quite remarkable, and we shall dwell for a moment on the psychologic implications of this feature of the baby's cry. Table II shows the decibel levels of noises from various sources and locations. It can be seen that the cry sound (averaging 84 decibels when measured 10 inches from the mouth) approaches in intensity those high-energy noises listed at the top of the table. The cry is 20 decibels louder than ordinary speech, which assures its priority over other acoustic signals in communication. Crying easily cuts through the sound of adult conversation and may even mask parts of it (see Chapter 9). One can now appreciate why a parent must interfere with the baby's crying: this sound is too annoying to be tolerated beyond a short period of time, particularly at close range (16). Thus a cry cries to be turned off! The listener who cannot escape usually reduces the noise by soothing whatever baby-needs occasion it. A less desirable alternative is found in certain post-partum illnesses. Here the mother reduces instead her contact with reality to avoid the responsibility of caring for a child. Turning off the auditory intake system and focussing on hallucinatory voices may be part of this abnormal reaction (86). Intolerance to the cry of the baby is very frequently reported after attacks upon infants, and infanticides (25).

INDIVIDUAL CHARACTERISTICS OF CRIES

We already noted from octave band measurement that, in spite of certain acoustic similarities, there are also demonstrable differences between the cries of individual babies. Some babies produce a pleasantly musical sound, others a more scream-like cry, while still others make squawking, whiny, or guttural noises. These different patterns will undoubtedly be studied acoustically in future research, since it is important to know how various forms of infantile soundmaking are related to the preverbal expression of affect (115).

A fundamental question that needs study in this connection is whether genetic factors account for some of the differences in infantile soundmaking. It is already known that identical (one-egg) twins sound more alike *as adults* than do fraternal (two-egg) twins (47); identical twins also are more similar in their vocal range, voice quality, vital pulmonary capacity, and larynx size (76). What (if any) genetic determinants stimulate such similarities and differences among twins, and how does upbringing influence their soundmaking behavior?

This problem was approached through a study of thirty-two infant twins—sixteen same-sex pairs—whose zygosity was unknown at the time of the study (93). The cries were tape-recorded in the hospital nursery or at home within the first month and analyzed in terms of three criteria:

1. Acoustic—half-octave band measurements of the cry peaks (8 points)
2. Musical—the rhythm, pitch, and speed patterns of the cries (8 points)
3. Phonetic—the phonetic characteristics of the cries (4 points)

The task of the investigators was to try to match their zygosity predictions based on these twenty similarity—dissimilarity points with the results of blood-type determinations of zygosity. These were the results:

Half-octave band measurement correctly differentiated some one-egg twin pairs from two-egg pairs. In such instances the identical twins cried with the same loudness, and showed similarities in number, location, and appearance of energy peaks along the acoustic frequency spectrum. Musical and phonetic analyses of the cries also enabled us to correctly predict zygosity in some instances. Certain one-egg pairs cried with the same tones, rhythm, and timing, and resembled each other phonetically, while some of the two-egg twins were clearly different. But a statistical study* showed that zygosity predictions based on the soundmaking of these infants did not go beyond chance levels of predictability. Some of the one-egg twins cried in ways that were much less alike than the cries of some of the two-egg pairs. It remains to be seen therefore to what extent the soundmaking of young

---

*The Mann-Whitney U Test, with significance set at .05, was applied to a ranking of the twin pairs on the basis of three different criteria, and also on the basis of overall similarity-dissimilarity scores (118).

babies is influenced by genetic processes underlying their physical development and to what extent crying is further affected by physiologic and emotional dynamics unrelated to heredity.

SUMMARY

The first meaningful sound anyone makes is the cry, an acoustic pattern this chapter describes in detail. While this sound has many general features of any acoustic stimulus, viz. the capacity to arouse, to alert, and to direct a listener, it also has certain unique informative properties which cause listeners to recognize a situation of need and alarm. Acoustic measurements of baby cries are presented with the aim of specifying what some of these properties may be. The individual variability of crying is also discussed, and some preliminary statements are made about the relationship between crying and other aspects of infant behavior. I also review here a study of twin babies which focusses on the question of whether crying has a genetic component. Soundmaking might prove to be a useful intervening variable for future studies of the relationship between genetic patterns and human behavior.

Chapter 5

SPEECH

Speech is undoubtedly the most complex form of soundmaking ever devised. From an evolutionary standpoint it is uniquely human: man and animal both may bark, twitter, grunt, and make noises, but only humans can emit the elaborately organized sound chains called spoken language.

Chapter 2 explained that speech makes use of acoustic building blocks called phonemes. The number of phonemes in any language is surprisingly small, varying from 15 to 100 in different languages throughout the world (58). But learning to combine these few sounds into meaningful verbal statements may take a lifetime. A child starts to speak by imitating sounds of his elders; he unconsciously comes to recognize some of the linguistic rules for organizing the sounds into words and sentences (19). School, college, vocation, and social experience later influence how a growing person speaks, and what he speaks about (119).

DENOTATIVE AND EMOTIVE SPEECH

The phonemics and grammar of a language are relatively fixed and change little over the years (50). For example, in order to convey my hunger for an apple to another person, I must say "I want to eat an apple," and not something like "Opal vaunts heat eyes." Semantics of language is more fluid however; the referential properties of words can change quickly, depending on when one speaks, where, with whom, and under what social conditions. Under totalitarian regimes, for instance, words like individuality, state, and community mean something quite different than in democracies (79). Particularly transcendental terms like liberty, freedom, toleration, etc. are difficult to define meaningfully. In the end one consults a dictionary to define a word, and dictionaries are in reality albums of speech-sound-clusters (words) listed with all the different things these words denote.

Before the days of radio, cinema, television, and other mass communication media, it must have been a relatively simple task to write a dictionary. One could cull the various meanings of words from their usage in written texts, the main vehicle for distance communication then available. But today the reading of books, letters, and other written materials is not the predominant way to exchange information. There is much more emphasis on actually looking at and listening to what goes on in the world. Travel is easier, and those who do not travel can vicariously look and listen to happenings elsewhere by turning on the television set or going to the movies. As peoples' life experience thus broadens, the number of things they make sounds about becomes much greater, and the job of the dictionary to define these sounds grows accordingly. Lately dictionaries have even come to include so-called slang expressions—the words that people use when they want to breach the longwinded fussiness of formal speech (138).

The psychiatrist, whose job is to find out how people feel and to correct any abnormal emotional reactions, must speak with his patients. The fuzzy boundary between denotative and emotive speech (20) does not make this a particularly easy undertaking. In contrast to other listeners, a psychiatrist when he listens to what a patient says cannot be content with general, dictionary-defined, denotative significance of words. He must find out precisely the emotive significance of any particular patient's soundmaking, lest its conventional denotative meaning is used to evade embarrassing topics and thus avoid emotionality (37).

A common practice among psychiatrists for penetrating the facade of conventional meaning inherent in speech is to pay very close attention to what a patient does while speaking. One tries to note all aspects of the speaker's behavior, watches for squirms, grimaces, hoarseness, stammering, and other signs, and then scans this information for clues to the referential-level of the words used (109). For example, the doctor may find that Mrs. Smith says she "feels fine," but the *tremulousness of her voice* and the *anguished expression on her face* tell him that she is not at all convinced of this and may in fact be struggling with feelings of tension and anxiety. These nonverbal signs—*tremulous voice and anguished expression*—enable the doctor to correctly recognize that the verbal sign "feels fine" refers not to Mrs. Smith but to some imaginary person whom Mrs. Smith is trying—for reasons possibly of pride, embarrassment, or self-deceit—to describe to the doctor. The first symptom, *tremulous voice,* is a nonverbal acoustic sign, while the second, *anguished expression,* is a nonverbal gesture. Both convey emotive meaning.

STEREOTYPED SOUNDMAKING

T. H. Pear was one of the first investigators to scientifically study nonverbal acoustic behavior. He conducted an experiment over the BBC in England: on three successive nights a speech sample was broadcast by several different speakers, and radio listeners were asked to judge each speaker's sex, age, vocation, leadership experience, birthplace, and localities that might have influenced the way of speaking (97). Over 4,000 reports were sent in, and while some listeners correctly guessed some of the speaker characteristics, there were also many errors. Certain of these errors were remarkably consistent; for instance 50 percent of the listeners thought a detective to have an outdoor job like farming. Pear's experiments were repeated in the United States by Cantril and Allport. They concluded that a speaker's nonverbal soundmaking reveals reliable information about age, occupation, and appearance, is occasionally helpful for evaluating personality attributes like extraversion and dominance, but may be misleading in regard to other speaker characteristics (21).

It has gradually become clear from these and other studies that while speech patterns may become stereotyped and thus easy to identify, the stereotype itself does not necessarily relate directly to any single aspect of the speaker's background, physique, or personality pattern (66). Indeed, at times an acoustic stereotype may reflect the listener's limited or idiosyncratic exposure to certain forms of soundmaking, rather than be a function of discernible relationships between speech and speaker. For example, in the United States, acoustic stereotypes like the *hillbilly* (Mortimer Snerd), the *politician* (Throckmorton P. Guildersleeve), the *gangster* (Humphrey Bogart), the *seductress* (Marlene Dietrich), and the *housewife* (Ma Perkins), probably dominate the auditory judgments of anyone who regularly listened to the radio before the TV days. Acoustic stereotypes are helpful or harmful, depending on how they are used and by whom. In medical work, for instance, the characteristic sound of aortic insufficiency may help a careful physician to rule out other cardiac conditions and to make a correct diagnosis. Popular judgments based on acoustic perceptions may on the other hand be misleading and dangerous—"she sounds mad," "he sounds like a communist."

An amusing and often amazingly accurate way to portray the stereotyped soundmaking of certain speakers is in terms of musical instruments. Because of their fixed construction, these instruments are limited in soundmaking to certain ranges of intensity, pitch, tone, and shapes (87). An 18th Century Englishman (who called himself Nicholas Humdrum) wrote two articles in *The Tattler* which very elegantly describe conversationalists as though these were musical instruments, each emitting a particular kind of sound. On April Fool's Day, 1710, this mischievous writer pointed out that each person "plays upon such a particular instrument as is the most suitable to his character, and expresses that style and manner. . . . which is peculiar to him." He then described ten such patterns of soundmaking in detail:

1. *"Your Drums* are the blusterers in conversation, that, with a loud laugh, unnatural mirth, and a torrent of noise, domineer in public assemblies; overbear men of sense; stun their companions; and fill the place they are in with a rattling sound. . . ."

2. *"The Lute. . .* sounds very finely by itself. Its notes are exquisitely sweet, and very low, easily drowned in a multitude of instruments, and even lost among the few, unless you give a particular attention to it. . . The lutenists therefore are men of a fine genius, uncommon reflexion, great affability, and esteemed chiefly by persons of a good taste, who are the only proper judges of so delightful and soft a melody."

3. *"The Trumpet* is . . . capable of exquisite turns and modulations. The gentlemen who fall under this denomination are your men of the most fashionable edu-

cation, and refined breeding, who have learned a certain smoothness of discourse, and sprightliness of air,
from the polite company they have kept but at the
same time they have shallow parts, weak judgements
and a short reach of understanding."

4. "*Violins* are the lively, forward, importunate wits,
    that distinguish themselves by the flourishes of imagin-
    ation, sharpness of repartee, glances of satire, and
    bear away the upper part in every consort. I cannot
    however but observe that when a man is not disposed
    to hear music, there is not a more disagreeable sound
    in harmony than that of a Violin."

5. ". . . . your *Bass-viol* . . . grumbles in the bottom of
    the consort, and with a surly masculine sound
    strengthens the harmony, and tempers the sweetness
    of the several instruments that play along with it. The
    Bass-viol . . . may signify men of rough sense and un-
    polished parts; who do not love to hear themselves
    talk, but sometimes break out with an agreeable blunt-
    ness, unexpected wit, and surly pleasantries, to the no
    small diversion of their friends and companions. In
    short, I look upon every sensible true-born Briton to
    be naturally a Bass-viol."

6. "As for your rural wits, who talk with great eloquence
    and alacrity of foxes, hounds, horses, quickset hedges,
    and six-bar gates, double ditches, and broken necks, I
    am in doubt whether I should give them a place in the
    conversable world. However, if they will content
    themselves with being raised to the dignity of *Hunting-
    horns*, I shall desire for the future, that they be known
    by that name."

7. ". . . the *Bagpipe* species will entertain you from morn-
    ing to night with the repetition of a few notes, which
    are played over and over, with the perpetual humming
    of a drone running underneath them. These are your
    dull, heavy, tedious story tellers, the load and burden
    of conversations, that set up for men of importance, by
    knowing secret history, and giving an account of trans-

actions, that, whether they ever passed in the world or not, doth not signify a halfpenny to its instructions, or welfare."

8. "There are so few persons who are masters in every kind of conversation and can talk on all subjects, that I do not know whether we should make a distinct species of them. Nevertheless, that my scheme may not be defective, for the sake of these few who are endowed with such extraordinary talents, I shall allow them to be *Harpsichords,* a kind of music which everyone knows is a consort by itself."

9. "As for your *Passing-Bells,* who look upon mirth as criminal, and talk of nothing but what is melancholy in itself, and mortifying to human nature, I shall not mention them."

10. "I shall likewise pass over in silence all the rabble of mankind, that crowd our streets, coffee-houses, feasts, and public tables. I cannot call their discourse conversation, but rather something that is practised in imitation of it. For which reason, if I would describe them by any musical instrument, it should be by those modern inventions of the *bladder and strings, tongs and key, marrow-bone and cleaver* (124)."

ACOUSTIC MEASUREMENT OF SPEECH

Speech consists of sequences of phonetic sound interrupted by silences. Studied acoustically, the sound of speech has a specific configuration of *distinctive features,* twelve to fifteen of which suffice to characterize just about all phonemes of all languages of the world (58). If you run a speech segment through a set of acoustic filters, intensity levels as measured in different bands may fluctuate from moment to moment depending on the distinctive features of the phonemes being filtered. How could one characterize in acoustic terms the human being who produces the speech rather than the phonemic variability of speech he emits?

The solution, through perhaps unpalatable for a linguist, is one which comes readily to an acoustician, particularly if he is familiar with Nicholas Humdrum's ingenious approach to sound-makers as musical instruments: ignore the phonemic variability of speech and treat the sound as a form of noise. If one assumes that human beings are one species of noisemaker, it is possible to measure their speech as one measures other noises, say those of steam-engines, drills, or jet-planes. Rapid momentary fluctuations of acoustic energy can then be ignored, and the acoustic energy levels can be measured in ways described in Chapter 3 and already applied to the analysis of the baby cries. Most speakers seem to sustain a relatively uniform flow of sound for two to four seconds, about the time it takes to exhale. For acoustic analysis one cuts pieces of speech four seconds in duration from the master tape-recordings. Each piece is spliced together, making one continuous loop of tape which is analyzed by the H. H. Scott Sound Analyzer (88). The *slow* setting of the Sound Analyzer is used to dampen the excursion of the needle in the decibel-meter. This automatically dilutes the effects on momentary energy-level fluctuations of brief silences and of phonemic variability during the four-second intervals. A further aid in studying speech sound acoustically is to run the tapes *backwards* through the machine. This reduces all sounds to a meaningless noise, and prevents the acoustician from being distracted in his measurements by what the tape-recorded person is saying.

Half-octave band measurements obtained in this way show acoustic energy levels of speech to be higher in certain frequency bands than in others, much like the peaks which were found in half-octave band studies of baby cries discussed in Chapter 4. *The energy peaks in half-octave band analysis of speech will be called "motants."* This term is used to suggest that possibly emotive sounds have specific acoustic structures, as do speech sounds according to studies done with the sound spectrograph. Spectrographic studies use the term "formant" to refer to acoustic energy-level peaks (42). The relationship between motants and formants remains to be worked out in future research. At the present time the significance of the different motants (see Chapter 6) remains speculative.

Motant 1 is the first energy peak to show up, reading from left (low-frequency) to right (high-frequency) along the acoustic spectrum. It most likely represents that part of the speech signal which carries energy from phonation, the contribution of lungs and larynx to speech. The horizontal position of motant 1 along the spectrum is a function of the vibration rate of the vocal folds in the pulmonary air-column; its vertical position (height) along the intensity axis represents the forcefulness of the passing stream of air pushed out by the lungs. Motant 1 usually contains the fundamental tone of the speech sound. This has potential psychiatric significance in the sense that the position of the fundamental tone in the voice is largely responsible for the judgement whether a person is a "bass," "baritone," "tenor," "alto," or "soprano." Bass voices and baritones are regularly associated with post-pubertal males, while sopranos indicate females and children. Tenor and alto voices, while they may lean definitely in the male or the female direction, often convey a sense of undifferentiation or immaturity that may be clinically important (82). When a voice is low-pitched, motant 1 appears further to the left of the curve than when a voice is high-pitched, as for example the baby cry, with its first motant at 500 cps.

Motant 2 is the prominent energy peak to the right of motant 1 in half-octave band analyses of speech. It seems to denote primarily that portion of the speech signal which represents acoustic resonance energy. What is psychiatrically of interest about motant 2 is that this energy peak fluctuates as a function of the "powerfulness" of a speaker's voice, a useful diagnostic criterion. When patients speak energetically and enthusiastically they produce more resonance energy and have a prominent, full, wide, second motant. At such times, motant 2 may even fuse with motant 1, creating a "robust" acoustic pattern (see Chapter 6). On the other hand, when patients speak in a subdued manner they emit less resonance energy. In some such instances motant 2 is lower or may even disappear, giving the acoustic curve a "hollow" configuration (see Chapter 6).

Motant 3 is a peak or an abrupt change in the intensity levels of half-octave band speech analyses usually located between 1,000 and 2,000 cps. Its psychiatric significance is unknown at this time. Possibly motant 3 has something to do with a peculiar voice quality that speech therapists call "oral voice" and psychiatrists associate with infantile behavior.

Motant 4 is a peak of energy concentration at the upper-frequency end of the half-octave band analysis, to the right of motant 3. The production of sibilance and friction sound at the front of the mouth seems to be responsible for the acoustic energy located here. Motant 4 is difficult to measure accurately. In poorly-articulated speech little energy actually comes through at this level; on the other hand, when a person suddenly emphasizes s, z, ch, or other hissing consonant sounds, motant 4 may momentarily become so powerful that it is difficult to get any steady decibel reading. These phonologic criteria also indicate something about the potential psychiatric significance of motant 4, since it objectively demonstrates the "noise-making" component of speech. Harsh or overemphatic front-articulation will add sudden jolts of acoustic energy to motant 4. So will giggling, splutters, coughs, whispers, and other acoustic manifestations of emotion.

SUMMARY

This chapter tackles the problem of speech, which, as Sir Russell Brain has pointed out, lends itself well to detailed study but is so complex that underlying principles are often difficult to formulate. I continue here to attempt a delineation between denotative and emotive soundmaking. Denotative speech is defined as that portion of verbal behavior which can be understood by reference to vocabulary, grammar, and other formal rules of language. Emotive speech starts with transcendental words and phrases capable of rapid fluctuations in meaning, and goes on to the borderland of linguistics, the new area of paralanguage that linguists and anthropologists are currently trying to define. Beyond this lies the nonverbal soundmaking of children and such emotional expressions as laughter and crying. Physicians are concerned with this aspect of soundmaking since it provides clues for the evaluation of health and disease in patients.

If one analyzes speech acoustically, it is possible to demonstrate foci of sound energy located at certain points along the frequency spectrum. Studied spectrographically, these foci are called *formants*; their shape, size, position, and inter-relationships account for the "distinctive features" which make phonemes recognizable. Since a half-octave band method rather than spectrography is used in the following chapters, I have decided to call these foci *motants*. The relationship between formants and motants is unknown at present. I have presented some suggestions as to the possible clinical significance of certain motant patterns. In the next three chapters, we shall see to what extent the acoustic structure of speech as analyzed in terms of half-octave band sound energy levels can be correlated with certain aspects of the behavior and psychopathology of speakers.

Chapter 6

FOUR ACOUSTIC STEREOTYPES

This chapter presents half-octave band measurements of sound produced by 26 individuals, mostly psychiatric patients in the hospital or clinic. Methods for tape-recording and acoustic analysis outlined at the end of Chapter 3 were used in all cases. At the present stage of research in psychiatry it is not yet possible to demonstrate in detail the acoustic correlates for all psychopathologic emotional states described clinically. But one can specify acoustically a number of stereotyped forms of soundmaking which are often encountered in clinical work and which physicians will readily recognize. Four such stereotypes are summarized here, each followed by its acoustic analogue and additional clinical examples.

THE SHARP VOICE

This acoustic stereotype defines a kind of sound which nonverbally carries the message "help me." It is a sound indicative of trouble, no matter how calm or uninformative the words used by the patient may be. Many physicians can spot this sound on the telephone, and may use it as a clue to the seriousness of the call. Patients who frequently use a sharp voice easily make themselves heard in hospital wards and clinic waiting rooms; their sound has a way of penetrating through the racket of noisy environments. Often such patients are called annoying; their behavior may be manipulative, self-seeking, and aggressive. Other adjectives frequently attached to the soundmaking of this group—which includes, hysterical, schizophrenic, and other diagnostic subgroups—are complaining, querulous, helpless, and infantile.

A psychoneurotic patient referred to the out-patient clinic for help with numerous emotional problems became the first subject with a sharp voice to be sudied acoustically (88). Her primary complaint was obesity, a condition which had failed for many years to respond to diet, medication, and other therapeutic measures.

The patient had an unhappy childhood. Her father having died shortly after the birth of a younger brother, she was sent to a foster home. There the girl first started to overeat, in an attempt to offset nutritionally the emotional cravings occasioned by separation from her mother. During adolescence she was allowed to return home, but by now the mother had remarried and was more interested in the new husband than in the two children from her first marriage. Of these, the stepfather preferred the younger brother, thus adding to the patient's sense of isolation and loneliness. The girl now hit upon a terrible solution: she decided to play the mother's rival and try to seduce her stepfather. She went on a crash diet, groomed herself, and adopted all the mannerisms of a temptress. Unfortunately the stepfather could not see through this adolescent play-acting. A rather pompous and self-centered man, he felt flattered by what he took to be real affection, encouraged the girl's eroticism, and finally drove her out of the house in panic by attempting clumsily to entice her into sexual activity.

This second rejection the lovestarved adolescent could not take. She resumed her overeating, and in addition got herself pregnant by an older man who was already married. Her mother was aghast at this situation, but the stepfather, who had never had children of his own, welcomed the illegitimate mother and continued his flirtation with her under the guise of being paternal. After the birth of her child, the patient sought psychiatric help. She was 60 pounds overweight, gorged herself daily on ice cream and candy bought with her meager allowance, and felt alternating dependent affection and rivalrous hostility towards her helpless mother.

The patient visited the clinic once a week for psychotherapeutic interviews. During part of each interview a tape-recording of her spontaneous conversational speech was made. Half-octave band measurements of nine weekly samples are shown in Figure 8. Some similarities between the various curves are apparent when one tabulates the center frequencies of half-octave bands in which the motants are located:

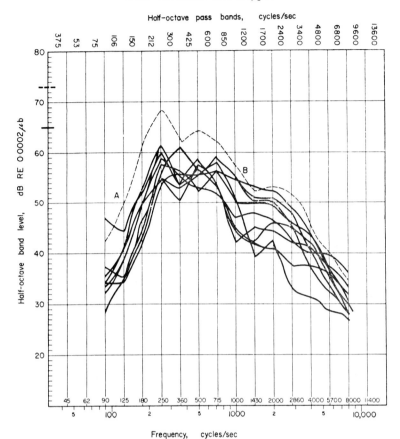

Fig. 8. Weekly analyses of the sound of a twenty-two year old obese woman in psychotherapy, showing a basic pattern resembling that of a ten
year old child (AB) and irregularities which probably represent her
dramatic aggressive use of the voice.

Interview Number	Motant 1	Motant 2	Motant 3*
1	250 cps	715 cps	2000 cps
2	250	500	1430
3	250	500-1000	2000
4	360	715	2000
5	250	500	2000
6	250	—	1430
7	360	715	—
8	250	715	2000
9	250	500	—

*Motant 4 is too weak to be accurately located.

Six of the nine interviews show motant 2 to be exactly one octave higher than motant 1. For example, interview 2 has motant 1 in the half-octave band centered at 250 cps while motant 2 is centered at 500 cps; interviews 4 and 7 have motant 1 at 360 cps and motant 2 at 715 cps, again a space of one octave. This acoustic structure in the patient's sound is itself of interest, although we do not know yet how to explain it adequately. Reinforcing the octave overtones of a fundamental is well-known to bring about considerable strengthening of a sound (54); it is often used by singers and instrumental musicians to enrich a musical structure and may also be part of the mechanism whereby this patient makes herself heard.

In addition to the octave pattern already noted, Figure 8 shows a kind of jaggedness which we earlier came to associate with the cries of babies (see Chapter 4). Assuming this characteristic of the half-octave band measurement curves to be indicative of a childish quality audible in the patient's voice, I compared these with measurements of the sound emitted by a much younger patient. This was a ten year old boy, referred to the psychiatric clinic specifically because of an aggressive way of speaking. His frequent hurling of obscenities at his parents had raised the question of Gilles de la Tourette Disease, a syndrome of coprolalia and tics (32). Acoustic study of this boy revealed a pattern very similar to that of the obese woman: the first motant was located at 250 cps, and motant 2 was at 500 cps, one octave higher. To demonstrate similarities between the adult patient's sharp voice and the sound emitted by the little boy, his acoustic curve is superimposed on Figure 8, elevated by eight decibles in order to make it stand out from the patient's curves. It is easy to see the first two motants separated by one octave; I call this configuration *the twin peaks effect.*

The twin peaks effect may be one characteristic that distinguishes the sharp voice from other acoustic stereotypes presented later. Twin peaking has been found in subsequent half-octave band measurements of the sound presented by patients with various other emotional problems. Six examples will follow here; they are illustrated acoustically in Figure 9. The significance of these patterns will be further discussed in Chapter 8.

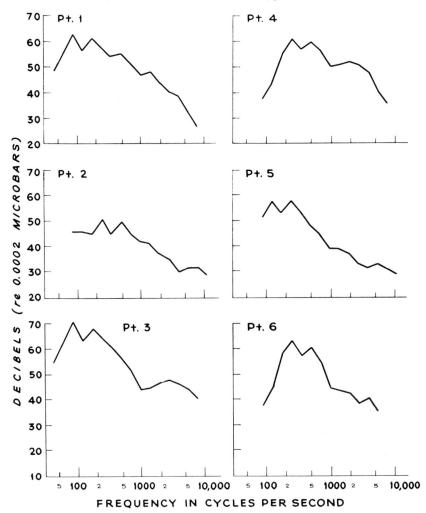

Fig. 9. Examples of half-octave band measurements of sound from six different psychiatric patients. Note the prominent twin-peak octave resonance pattern.

Patient 1.

A thirty-five year old salesman, this rotund, profusely sweating man has been out of commission for several years because of symptoms of depression. He describes himself as "very emotional" and is aware of a "desperate," "sincere," "scary" tone quality in his voice. The product of a powerful father and a timid mother, this man has never developed much personal independence. Experienced at clinging to two sisters for support in childhood, he has failed to establish an adult orientation toward his own wife and children.

The patient speaks volubly and fluently, especially about himself, but with a tremulous voice that one associates with anxiety. He uses many dramatic, aggressive gestures, and mannerisms which make others feel quite uncomfortable. Half-octave band measurement shows a prominent first motant centered at 90 cps, and another energy peak one octave higher, at 180 cps. (This acoustic analysis also has certain features of the "flat voice" to be discussed later: resonance energy sags and produces a flatness in the curve.) Motant 3 peaks at 1430 cps.

Patient 2.

This thirty year old farmer's wife was sent to a speech therapist because of an extremely squeezed, hoarse, subdued speech sound. An underlying emotional problem was immediately recognized, and the patient was referred for psychiatric evaluation. The woman is paranoid and delusional. She wants to study veterinary medicine because of a sore back due to beatings administered by her father years ago. She also complains of lumps on her fingers and begs for an operation to have these removed. (Some weeks later a surgeon unwisely consented to do this, but a florid schizophrenic excitement developed during anesthetization.)

During my interview with her before the onset of overt psychosis, this patient speaks with a voice that sounds like a choking baby. She repeatedly tries to clear her throat, without relief. Tears come occasionally as she reveals her unhappy frame of mind, and these crying spells bring about a very brief but only partial relief of the croaky sound. Half-octave band measurement shows a voice of low overall intensity (64 phons).* Motant 1 is at 250 cps, and motant 2 at 500 cps. Motant 3 does not clearly show up. Motant 4 shows as a bulge between 4,000 and 11,400 cps.; this probably denotes the uncomfortable sounding, raspy noise in this patient's markedly abnormal speech.

---

* The phon is a loudness-level unit. It is derived from a summation of constituent half-octave band decibel measurements according to a formula devised by S. S. Stevens (126).

Patient 3.

This belligerent, twenty year old, foreign-born laborer was injured during an adolescent motor-cycle accident which damaged both frontal lobes. After a coma he laboriously relearned to speak English, but a residual spastic hemiplegia makes him unfit for work. This increases an already troublesome friction in the patient's subtly erotic relationship with his widowed mother. Unsuccessful with girls, he is also deeply disturbed by conscious homosexual desires.

In speaking, this patient uses surprisingly big words and accurate grammar; but the words come out slowly and what he says tends to sound pedantic and artificial. He apologizes frequently and complains about being stared at. His voice sounds monotonous and seems to contain a kind of low-pitched growl. Half-octave band measurement shows a steep first motant at 90 cps. The second twin-peak at 180 cps is motant 2. (Acoustic energy falls off precipitously in the mid-region of the spectrum in a way that is very suggestive of the "hollow voice" pattern to be discussed later.) A concentration of acoustic energy centered at 2,860 cps may represent this patient's quite prominent articulatory noise pattern—partly due to badly fitting dentures. It probably is motants 3 and 4 fused into one large energy region.

Patient 4.

This twenty-eight year old housewife twitches and jumps nervously, but has no actual convulsions. Her problem is how to get along with people, but she requests psychotherapy specifically for "my tic." Since age ten she has experienced recurrent spasms of her arms, face, and entire body. Diagnosed as an extrapyramidal syndrome, this condition usually becomes much worse when tensions arise at home, where she incompetently cares for a large family.

In the interview she rambles in a girlish, prattling way about her sex life, her dreams, and about how at ten months "I trained my mother to regulate by bowel habits." Throughout her recital there are squeaks, splutters, giggles, stammers, and other noises. She voices many platitudes, and her ideas, while coherently stated, sound confused. Confrontation with reality problems makes her angry and defensive. Half-octave band measurement of this patient's speech sound shows the sharp twin-peaks of motant 1 at

250 cps and motant 2 at 500 cps. A swollen energy region (probably motants 3 and 4) indicates that a considerable amount of noise is also emitted in the higher-frequency portion of the acoustic spectrum, perhaps because of the giggly quality in her voice.

Patient 5.

This sensitive, seventeen year old, effeminate schoolboy has been raised in fifteen different foster homes after his parents were divorced when he was four years old. Both parents are artistically gifted but eccentric. The patient plays the piano, is socially withdrawn and isolated. His hospital admission came about in the following manner: for some time this boy was steeped in mystical religious thoughts and did not feel himself to be part of the world. With increasing urgency he experienced a desire to be dead. One night he climbed over the railing of a bridge well-liked by suicides; he dangled in empty space to feel what dying might be like. This behavior led to his being picked up by the police and brought to the hospital.

Supercilious and hostile, this patient speaks in a mincing, irritating manner. His word rate is rapid (average syllable duration was 0.12 seconds) and often the speech sounds tumble out of his mouth in a disorderly way that make it difficult to understand what he says. Half-octave band measurement of this speech reveals an overall low intensity, with motant 1 clearly defined at 125 cps and motant 2 one octave higher, at 250 cps. Intensity levels of these motants is identical, 58 decibels, giving a typical twin peak. Intensity thereafter falls off precipitously, and the middle of the frequency spectrum resembles the pattern of the "hollow voice." Some flattening is visible in the upper-frequency region, with a slight focussing of motant 4 at 5,700 cps. This may be indicative of an over-articulated, prissy quality in his speech sound.

Patient 6.

This distraught and restless thirty-two year old housewife claims she hears voices, and was originally brought to the clinic for evaluation of her hearing. Audiometric studies showed some sensory loss, but she was too disturbed to allow extensive studies. She angrily accused her husband of plotting against her. Following the birth of her first child ten years earlier she had developed some bizarre ideas and religiosity. Hospital care was necessary for several months, and over the intervening years she has several times been diagnosed to suffer from an advanced state of paranoid schizophrenia.

On examination the patient is tense, and inwardly preoccupied. There is a good deal of puzzlement, and she halfheartedly attempts to orient herself in an environment that is partly shut off to her because of deafness. Her responses to questions also indicate that her attention does not focus on what people say. Speech is hesitant and fragmented, and there is an acutely distressed quality to her voice. Half-octave band analysis shows motant 1 centered at 250 cps and motant 2 one octave higher, at 500 cps. There is then an abrupt drop of intensity, brought to a halt by motant 4 in the half-octave band centered at 4,000 cps.

THE FLAT VOICE

Another acoustic stereotype commonly encountered in medical practice is the sound of patients who are listless, resigned, and depressed. No matter how convincingly such patients tell you (in words) that there is nothing the matter with them, their soundmaking says the opposite. This flabby, enervated, and sickly sound seems paralinguistically to announce the patient's dependency need and helplessness.

To explore the acoustic correlates of this form of behavior, a patient was studied who came to the clinic for the specific purpose of improving his speech. He was a lanky man in his twenties who complained "my wife tells me my voice is too soft. She gets angry because she can't understand what I say, and she also says I clear my throat too much." The patient himself did not appear much aware of the inadequate way he sounded, and only on his wife's recommendation did he decide to look into this problem. Many years had passed since another of his difficulties in communication—inability to spell—had been brought to his attention by a schoolteacher. Whereas he had excelled in arithmetic, drawing, and mechanics, in the fifth grade a "bad teacher" had made him repeat a year of school because of the incompetence in spelling.

The patient talked freely about himself, making it possible to trace some of the essential factors in his personal life development. His parents and grandparents had been farmers, Protestant, poor people. Mother was overtly the more influential parent; she directed the household and helped earn money. Father was overtly passive; he paid little attention to the children, except to beat them whenever mother prescribed this punishment. The patient was the youngest of four sons, and felt he was expected to satisfy the parents' frustrated desire for a daughter. He was mother's little helper in the kitchen, assisted her with the canning of fruits and vegetables, and usually waited on the older men at the table.

As he grew up, the patient remained uncertain about his sexual identity and became a rather passive, selfconscious, and uncomfortable adolescent. In high school he was able to hide his feminine interests by participating in athletics, and he excelled as a football player. Another important stabilizing influence was an interest in coins: since adolescence the patient has worked diligently on a coin collection, and he is now an expert who can spot a valuable coin immediately and arrange profitable swaps. Having no particularly strong ambitions and feeling dissatisfied with life at home on the farm, the patient joined the Army shortly after his high school graduation.

After his release from the service, the patient, who had never had sexual relations, lived in the small apartment of his best friend, an unhappily married man on the verge of breaking up with his wife. Explosive tensions developed in this triangle situation, the patient becoming the target of abuse from his friend and of seductive advances from the wife, who subsequently got a divorce and married him. On the surface this marriage appears satisfactory, but actually the patient's wife, an older, demanding, and insecure woman, finds him wanting in many respects besides the soundmaking which occasioned psychiatric referral. She constantly criticizes him, thereby interfering with what little leadership he is capable of.

The patient's physical appearance is striking: he is an elongated, slightly stooped, thin man; his face is pale, smooth, and childlike; his eyes are tearful; and his gestures and body movements are sluggish, inexpressive, and feeble. For the acoustic analysis of his soundmaking, he was asked, after each weekly psychotherapy interview, to tape-record the following paragraph:

"Around the turn of the century, a man decided to ship some sugar cane to Alaska. Before he set sail, many people asked to go along. A Methodist Episcopal minister told him that he wished to stop in San Francisco on the way. Once the crowd got aboard, there was no room for the cargo, and the man had to abandon his voyage. You can imagine how disappointed everyone was."

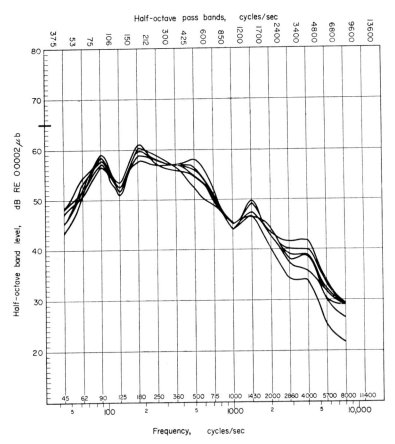

Fig. 10. Weekly acoustic analyses of the patient who complained of an inadequate voice are superimposed to demonstrate the lack of variation from one week to the next, and the smeared-out layer of acoustic energy between 180 and 500 cps.

Errors, mispronunciations, sighs, pauses, and other extra-linguistic phenomena audible on the tape-recordings were useful symptomatic clues to evaluate his emotional state throughout the course of treatment. The first four-second fragment of each tape-recording was also studied by means of half-octave band measurement. Figure 10 shows the results from six weekly recordings. There is little variation of intensity levels from one week to the next. The first motant is always located at 90 cps; the second motant seems in most of the curves to come to a peak at 180 cps, and then to drift off towards the right, coming gradually to a lower level. In some of the analyses there is a slight intensity peak at 500 cps. To remain consistent with the nomenclature as developed in Chapter 5, I shall call this entire energy component the second motant, with subpeaks at 180 cps and 500 cps. One might think of this configuration as acoustic energy which is smeared out rather evenly across a broad portion of the frequency spectrum. Flatness of the curve denoting this energy portion seems to be the distinguishing characteristic of the acoustic stereotype we are here dealing with. Motant 3, in contrast to the flat motant 2, is squeezed into a single half-octave band centered at 1,430 cps.

The following six patients, whose half-octave band analyses are illustrated in Figure 11, showed similarly flat curves and are therefore classed together under this acoustic stereotype.

Patient 1.

This prim, proper, pimply-faced twenty-five year old salesgirl had been told by an older, spinsterish lady at work that her speech was not properly pitched, baby-like, and sometimes unclear. The patient herself noted her voice at times to sound "too emphatic, like that of a school-teacher." She is an articulate person who enjoys talking but cannot relate more intimately to people. In spite of a core of femininity she has a kind of harsh, sand-papery surface which annoys men and keeps them at a distance.

Her acoustic behavior vacillates between a clipped and precise way of bringing out words, and a hesitant, holding-back manner of talking. There are many "uhs," and often her voice trails off before the end of phrases, giving a tentative air to what she says. Half-octave band measurement of a voice specimen during the interview shows motant 1 rather clearly defined at 180 cps. Motant 2 seems to be stretched flatly through a range of two octaves

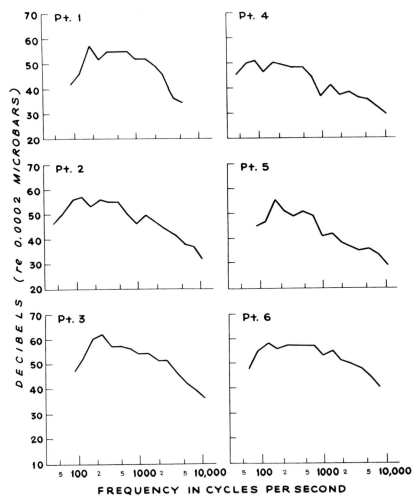

Fig. 11. Examples of half-octave band measurements of sound from six different psychiatric patients. Note the flatness of these curves, particularly in the center of the frequency spectrum.

without coming to a precise focus. The rest of the acoustic curve slopes; it does not show any definite 3rd or 4th motants.

Patient 2.

After a wildly-bleeding intestinal ulcer had brought him close to death, this twenty-six year old farmer voluntarily entered the psychiatric hospital for treatment of depression which in some obscure way appeared to be related to his somatic difficulties. He was aware of conflict over inability to spend enough time with his family in the face of an obsessive desire to provide well for them. He also suffers from extreme sensitivity about being slighted by other people, and feels an inner rage about being unable to predict exactly what is wanted from him. Occasional suicidal ideas have flashed through his mind.

During the interview he looks strong and healthy. The only external manifestations of depression are extremely timid gestures that belie his obvious physical strength. His voice is notably fuzzy; he sounds but does not look as demoralized and close to collapse as he is. Half-octave band measurement shows a rather broad first motant centered ambiguously at 125 cps. Motant 2 also lacks focus, coming to a small peak at 250 cps and remaining flat until it gets to 500 cps where the curve starts to drop steeply. Motant 3 shows up more definitely at 1,430 cps; then again there is a slope, but no clear 4th motant.

Patient 3.

A suspicious, agitated, retired sixty-five year old school principal, this acutely sick woman entered the hospital for electroconvulsive treatment of a depression. She had been orphaned before adolescence and her devout foster parents raised her to be an ardent, aggressive community leader. A marriage of ten years ended in the husband's suicide. After her daughter left home to get married, the patient deliberately planned for her own death, but continued to work as a teacher. Her overt psychiatric illness, an involutional psychotic reaction, began after retirement when her chronic depression was intensified by loneliness and social isolation.

At the time of the tape-recording, this patient is beset with paranoid ideas and, in the presence of otherwise intact intellectual functions, seems miserable and befuddled by what is happening. She repeatedly professes to have been a good person, thinks that others are driving her crazy, and begs for "another chance." She perceives the psychiatric examination as some kind of "mysterious" procedure, tries to overcome her fright by acting selfassured, and energetically objects to being tape-recorded. Half-octave band measurement shows motant 1 at 250 cps. The curve then drops and fails to show any other appreciable peaks of energy concentration. This pattern resembles another acoustic stereotype, the "hollow voice," which we shall discuss shortly.

Patient 4.

This daydreaming, shy, and confused college student experienced severe feelings of depression, indecisiveness, and guilt before his twenty-first birthday. Having been separated from his father for many years, he feels abnormally dependent on his mother and is fearful of going into the world of adults. His schoolwork is a mess, and he does now know where to turn.

A slight, cleancut, adolescent-looking boy, the patient speaks in a nasal voice, and with substandard articulation. He centers on himself in conversation to the point of boredom for others, and in spite of his claim to know what his problems are, cannot mobilize enough enthusiasm to attain immediate realistic goals, such as passing school examinations or going out on dates. Half-octave band measurement shows a sound of low overall intensity (63 phons). Motant 1, at 90 cps, indicates how low this sound is in pitch. Motant 2 stretches out, sags, and meanders on to 500 cps, where it starts to drop; this is the typical flat-voice pattern. Motant 3 has better definition, possibly because of the markedly nasal sound emitted by the patient.

Patient 5.

As a child and against her parents' wishes, this attractive twenty-four year old woman made up her mind to become an acrobat. She dieted throughout adolescence to reduce her rather large figure, and when admitted to the psychiatric hospital with a diagnosis of anorexia nervosa was vomiting after each meal. Menses and bowel movements had ceased months earlier. Sexual intercourse with her husband, a dairyman, had stopped shortly after their marriage a year before.

The patient looks willowy, girlish, and much too weak to cope with the rigors of the athletic training to which she feels committed. She seems friendly, yet distant. Clinging to her doctors in a childlike manner, she nevertheless defies them through selfinduced vomiting of her prepared diet. Her voice also sounds undernourished. Its half-octave band measurement shows a clear motant 1 at 180 cps, and a kind of lumpy motant 2 slightly peaked at 500 cps. The rest of the curve suggests the hollow voices to be described next, although motant 3 comes through somewhat better at 1,430 cps.

Patient 6.

Artistically inclined but forced into law through family pressures, this thirty-five year old attorney tried to reduce his disappointment with alcohol. Gradually his bleary eyes, florid face, and foul breath alerted coworkers to the difficulty.

The patient does not admit any trouble, and in psychotherapy discussions his manner becomes decidedly cocky. His gestures, actions, and tone of voice all betray markedly ambivalent attitudes. Thus in talking he sounds on the one hand brash, boastful, and berating, on the other fumbling and desperate. Half-octave band measurement of this patient's voice resembles—according to an acoustical engineer—the typically flat curve of "white noise." Only a shallow two-decibel wedge separates motant 1 from what seems to be the second motant smeared out over a range of over 2 octaves. Motant 3 is visible at 1,430 cps.

THE HOLLOW VOICE

The third acoustic stereotype to be portrayed by reference to case material and through half-octave band measurement is one which physicians encounter primarily in hospitals, especially around patients who are chronically ill. This is the lifeless, shattered, and empty sound often emitted by cachectic, debilitated, or stuporous patients. Initial studies of this sound showed only one formant, the first, and little or no resonance to form other energy peaks. This gave a pattern of precipitous *drop-off* in acoustic energy as one followed the curve from left to right.

It was first thought that this configuration might typify organic brain disease, since the first patients studied all had severe physical disturbances (89). But later on the drop-off pattern was also found in nonorganic problems. It seems therefore that hollow voices go with other appearances of generalized weakness, debility, depression, or profound fatigue than those specifically related to brain damage. As will be seen in later chapters, the hollow voice may even be produced by psychoneurotic patients during moments of inhibition when consciously or unconsciously the voice is used to convey a feeling of weakness. Figure 12 illustrates examples of patient-produced sound that conform to the hollow voice pattern.

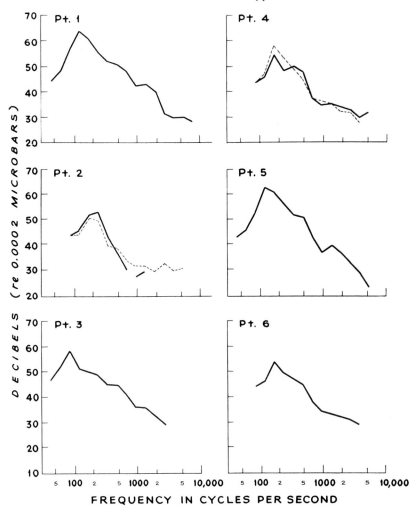

Fig. 12. Examples of half-octave band measurements of sound from six different psychiatric patients. Note the prominent drop-off in acoustic energy above the fundamental peak.

Patient 1.

This seventy-five year old man was brought to the hospital in a state of delirium near coma, in danger of dying. A bachelor, he has lain unfed and feverish in his hotel-room with an acute urinary tract infection. Examination shows him to be chronically ill, with signs of senile deterioration and generalized arteriosclerosis. He utters an inarticulate gibberish; no clear words can be detected in the unsteady rivulet of thready sound that issues from his edentulous mouth. As he improves with daily nursing care and treatment of his infection, some speech returns: he emits words, though these remain imbedded in a matrix of hoarse, fuzzy, sick-sounding vocalization.

Half-octave band measurement of this sound shows only a single point of effective energy concentration along the frequency spectrum. This is motant 1, the laryngeal fundamental, centered at 125 cps at an intensity level of 64 decibels. In higher reaches of the frequency spectrum, there is a precipitous and continuous drop of acoustic power. Motant 2, indicative of resonance energy of the voice, cannot be seen. Except for a slight recovery of acoustic energy in motant 3 at 1,430 cps, there is no appreciable high-frequency sound component. When I showed the analysis of this sound to an acoustical engineer who did not know what it denoted, he immediately remarked, "this looks like the sound of a wornout loudspeaker."

Patient 2.

Separated from her South American parents when she was seven and raised by a succession of nuns and maiden aunts, this twenty-one year old woman became a shy, seclusive person who seldom dated but lived alone with her fantasies. In the late teens she sought psychotherapy to understand various bodily feelings and sensations which did not make sense in the framework of religious and quasi-medical theories acquired in childhood. That there was an erotic component in her attitude towards men came into her awareness during interviews with an eager but inexperienced male psychiatric resident. She became panicky, thought she might die, and had to be hospitalized.

During interviews the patient resembles a terribly frightened bird. She looks as though she is about to take off, and indeed darts into the hall and tries to escape. Her conversation is sparse and non-revealing. When she does speak, it is with a sickly thin tone of voice, barely audible at times. Half-octave band measurement of her spontaneous speech shows only one focus of energy-concentration, motant 1 peaked at 250 cps. Immediately above this point, acoustic energy drops off precipitously and falls so low that it cannot even be measured above 850 cps, except for the band centered at 1,000 cps (28 decibels). To clarify the rest of the acoustic spectrum, it was necessary to analyze her reading voice (dashed curve) which is somewhat stronger, though still feeble. In addition to the fundamental tone concentration and the precipitous drop of energy already noted, the analysis of her reading voice shows some flatness between 1,000 and 5,700 cps, with a single focus of energy concentration at 2,860 cps.

Patient 3.

Periodically angry and depressed and subject to duodenal ulcers which necessitated a subtotal gastrectomy at sixty, this sixty-three year old truckdriver entered the hospital for treatment of a severe depression. He had been a good family man and steady worker until four months previously when he became unusually upset and angry at work, quit his job in a huff, and then found himself with nothing to do but brood and pace the floor. He talked of suicide and became a burden to his wife and their grownup children.

On admission this patient is neatly dressed and functions quite well intellectually, but appears severely shaken. He resembles someone who has recently witnessed a catastrophe. His skin is ashen and his eyes are fixed and sunken. While coherent, he mutters words in a lackluster way. The content of his available thoughts has to do with things he has done wrong, his sins and errors of the past. There is practically no variation in loudness, pitch pattern, and rhythm as he speaks; all sounds are on one hushed and monotonous level. Half-octave band measurement of this patient's sound shows the first motant coming to an abrupt peak at 90 cps, and then a steady downhill fall of energy across the frequency spectrum. A plateau in the octave 300 to 600 cps indicates a second focus of acoustic energy; there is another plateau in the octave 850 to 1,700 cps. Above 2,860 cps the intensity of this patient's speech sound is too low to register on the analyzer; total loudness is only 57 phons.

Patient 4.

Robbed of parental affection when her mother and father both died during her childhood, this thirty-four year old woman had married a widower twice her age and struggled for many years to manage the household and care for their nine children. She had a serious episode of ulcerative colitis, but recovered. After her husband was injured in an automobile accident and became aphasic, she found it increasingly difficult to organize her life. Instead of seeking help she plunged into more and more social and community activity. Also she turned her attention to the lives of female saints, regretting that she could not match their perfection. After some disruption in the sexual relationship with her husband, she tried to seduce a priest. Rapidly her reality contact broke down, and when hospitalized she was haggard, posturing, mute, and suspicious.

It takes an hour to extract enough speech from this patient for half-octave band measurement: a one second sentence, hoarsely muttered, "what do you want." This has the first motant centered at 180 cps, a humped second motant with its peak at 360 cps, and then an abrupt fall and flattening of the remainder of the acoustic energy curve. A second analysis, done on a sample of speech recorded when the patient agreed to read a printed paragraph, shows the hollow-voice pattern even more clearly (dashed curve). This time there is no differentiation of energy into first and second motants. Instead, a single focus (at 180 cps) locates the fundamental tone, followed by rapid decay of acoustic energy in the resonance area and higher frequency portions of the spectrum. Conversion of the curve into loudness units shows a level of only 58 phons.

Patient 5.

This sixty-four year old man was another of the patients with organic brain disease who showed the hollow voice pattern in half-octave band measurement. He had been a minister and in the past was very effective in using his voice to influence others. But after about his 55th year there was a gradual deterioration in functioning: he showed depression, apathy, emotional lability, and occasional mental clouding. Neurologic examinations revealed evidence of progressive ataxia, aphasia, and apraxia. Over the years he became untidy, and finally so helpless that hospital care became necessary.

This patient emits a stream of chaotic verbigeration that deals, when the content is recognizable, with themes of guilt, religion, and sin. While still somehow reminiscent of a sermon, the sound this patient produces is tired and weary; it also has a peculiar high-pitched metallic quality. Occasional bursts of uncontrolled weeping and crying interrupt this vocal sound. Half-octave band measurement shows a 63 decibel peak of motant 1 at 125 cps, followed by a steep drop in acoustic energy, a slight plateau in the octave 300-600 cps, then another steep drop, and a fairly prominent peak at 1,430 cps (motant 3).

Patient 6.

The most striking thing about this twenty year old secretary is that so little is known about her, as though she does not actually exist on this earth. Her parents were colorless, quiet people who have shifted their attitudes, places, and ways of living in accordance with the vicissitudes of social pressure. Her only brother is chronically schizophrenic in a State Hospital. After graduation from high school, the patient took a job as a secretary but felt vaguely ill. She seemed to belong nowhere, lacked strong emotions and interests, and felt related to nobody. To quiet a nagging sense of anguish she took alcohol and tranquilizers. A psychiatrist saw her in his office and encouraged her to become a person. He did not succeed, and she became instead a well-adjusted hospital inmate, quiet, rigidly conforming to the codes and rules laid down by the staff, and engaging mechanically in ironing, washing, and other cleanliness chores.

When interviewed for purposes of acoustic evaluation she looks mousy and speaks in a timid, halting, back-in-the-mouth way. The tone is colorless, the rhythm unorganized, and the phraseology stereotyped. Half-octave band measurement shows a sound of low intensity. Motant 1 is clearly defined at 180 cps. The downward slope characteristic of the hollow-voice pattern is again seen; there is no concentration of resonance energy to produce motant 2, nor does acoustic energy come to any focus in the frequency range above 1,000 cps; instead the curve flattens out as intensity levels drop from 34 to 29 decibels.

THE ROBUST VOICE

The robust voice refers to an acoustic stereotype which characterizes booming, impressive, successful-sounding voices. This sound may be emitted by persons who are, and those who pretend to be, extrovert, aggressive, and confident. Also the robust voice may be used in order to influence others, as in lectures, dramatization, or public speeches. The sound is loud but not unpleasant, resonant, and usually tonal. Its characteristic configuration on half-octave band measurement involves high levels of acoustic energy plus a rather symmetrical appearance of the curves, at times around a point where a relatively large amount of energy is concentrated. Figure 13 illustrates six such sounds.

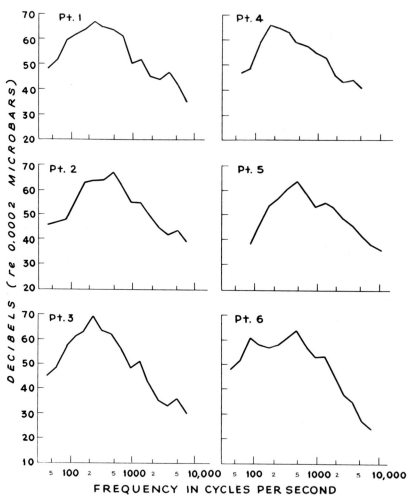

Fig. 13. Examples of half-octave band measurements of sound from six subjects who speak impressively. Note the high acoustic energy levels and the thick, symmetrical way energy is concentrated along the spectrum.

Subject 1.

A good sample of robust voice was obtained from a healthy Negro man of twenty-four, an orderly in the hospital. He is an overtly cheerful person whose resonant, booming voice is pleasant to listen to. It is the kind of smooth bass sound popular with amateur glee clubs. Half-octave band measurement shows a large concentration of energy defined by a semi-circular curve that comes to a slight peak in the band centered at 250 cps. This concentration of acoustic energy across almost 4 octaves spans the regions where the first and second motants are usually located. Apparently in this type of sound these discrete peaks are fused into one massive energy region. There is a clearly defined third motant at 1,430 cps and another peak (motant 4) at 4,000 cps. The total loudness of this acoustic sample is 77 phons.

Subject 2.

This is the speaking voice of an experienced schoolteacher, a sixty-two year old woman respected for her knowledge and highly regarded for her good judgment and skill with people. She often explains, lectures, and sometimes exhorts in a characteristically full and energetic sound. Half-octave band measurement shows a broad area of energy concentration on the lower-frequency side of the spectrum. A drop to a plateau in the octave 850-1,700 cps indicates the third motant. A peak centered at 5,700 cps locates the fourth motant, probably denoting this person's precise schoolteacherish articulation noise. This is a loud voice: 79 phons.

Subject 3.

Born in Bavaria, this eighty year old man has worked as a salesman and as a cook. He learned English in late adolescence and speaks with a slight stutter. He is a big exuberant man who loves to laugh, tell jokes, and sing. His voice is beery, his face florid, and his gestures are wide and dramatic. Half-octave band measurement shows a large concentration of sound energy defined by a semicircular curve with a superimposed peak in the band centered at 250 cps. This broad fusion of motants 1 and 2 covers close to four octaves, and slopes downward to a clearly-defined third motant in the half-octave band centered at 1,430 cps.

Subject 4.

A forty-five year old supervisor of nurses, this woman has a large body and a big voice, full, very audible, slightly shrill at times. It conveys a quality that some people associate with fervent devotion to duty and others with guilt-provoking complaint. Half-octave band measurement shows a single very large concentration of energy across more than 4 octaves of the frequency spectrum, coming to a focus in the half-octave band centered at 180 cps. No clear separation into discrete motants is seen except at the high-frequency end of the spectrum where there is a small peak at 4,000 cps. The sloping appearance of this curve is somewhat suggestive of the hollow voice pattern, but its overall intensity level is higher than one finds in these voices.

Subject 5.

This thirty-four year old Hungarian-born practical nurse has received psychiatric treatment for tension symptoms. She is an excitable and aggressive woman who speaks out loudly and forcefully. She is very verbal, enunciates clearly but with a foreign accent, and has a hearty, full tone of voice. Half-octave band measurement shows a pyramid-shaped concentration of energy extending from 150 cps to 1,200 cps, with a prominent peak in the band centered at 500 cps. It is not possible to make a distinction between first and second motants. There is a smaller peak at 1,430 cps, the usual place for motant 3, and then a gradual falling-off of acoustic energy in the upper-frequency region.

Subject 6.

This thirty-two year old psychiatrist has a baritone voice that sounds full and musical. He speaks rather slowly and selfconsciously, raising his voice when he wants to say something important. Half-octave band measurement shows motants 1 and 2 clearly defined and separated by a space of $2\frac{1}{2}$ octaves. The fundamental tone is located at 90 cps. Motant 2, denoting resonance energy, is located in the half-octave band centered at 500 cps. There is a plateau in the octave 850 to 1,700 cps, probably indicating motant 3.

SUMMARY

The notion of acoustic stereotypes having been presented as one useful approach to the problem of soundmaking, we start in this chapter to apply acoustic measurement to several specific sound patterns. Measurements of sound produced by an obese woman in psychotherapy and by six other psychiatric patients are presented in order to point out the possible significance of octave-reinforcement along the acoustic frequency spectrum. Flatness of the spectrum is demonstrated in seven patients, one of whom is discussed in greater detail since vocal inadequacy was his presenting symptom. Absence of acoustic resonance above the fundamental tone is another finding when the sound of certain sick persons is measured. A more robust, symmetrically distributed sound energy pattern is also discussed. The sounds analyzed in this chapter represent single cross-sectional samples from the acoustical behavior of different individuals. In some instances, the verbal content of these samples was held constant by having the subject read standard sentences. But since many other variables were uncontrolled, any possible relationship between sound-making and behavior discussed so far must remain hypothetical. The acoustic stereotypes delineated here represent a necessary first step if one wants to specify the distinctive acoustic properties of emotive sounds. The fact that this has already been done in the case of phonemic constituents in speech make me hopeful that it can also succeed for nonlinguistic aspects of soundmaking.

Chapter 7

ACOUSTIC CHANGES DURING
PSYCHOTHERAPY — A CASE STUDY

The preceding chapter delineated four acoustic stereotypes — sharp, flat, hollow, and robust voices. Twenty-two psychiatric patients and four nonpatients were briefly described, and half-octave band measurements of sound they produced during interviews were illustrated. If it were true that patients continuously emit the same kind of speech sound, we could now try to correlate these acoustic measurements with other personality characteristics of the disturbed and normal subjects. But people do not actually make the same sound all the time, no matter how stereotyped their behavior may be in other respects. In addition to linguistic variations which have already been mentioned, every speaker is influenced by a host of physiologic, psychic, and social factors, the specific effects of which upon soundmaking are not fully understood at present (90). Since human beings are neither jet planes that emit steady noises nor phonograph records that repeat the same sounds over and over again, one must interpret acoustic measurements of their soundmaking with caution.

This warning is particularly apt when one analyzes soundmaking during psychotherapy. Psychotherapy is a kind of behavior between two individuals specifically intended to improve the life of one (the patient) more profoundly than the life of the other (the doctor) (130). Only a few instances have been reported where therapy did not involve soundmaking, for example when treatment was conducted my mail (2) or by a deaf therapist (36). In most cases soundmaking is *an* if not *the* essential element of psychotherapy, since it is by speaking about himself that the patient informs the doctor of his problems, and it is by speaking about these problems that the doctor tries to help the patient (14).

In the course of such speeches patient and doctor may touch on things that are hard to define and that may not even be found in dictionaries—private fantasies, obscure feelings, and thoughts difficult to verbalize. No matter how hard he tries to get the patient to *talk about* these things, the therapist often is faced with the fact that the patient may *directly express* his problems through action (133). Whenever direct expression involves soundmaking—emotive soundmaking—acoustics has something tangible to contribute to psychotherapy: If the patient cannot put his problems into words but makes nonverbal sounds about them, the process of acoustic measurement may assist the translation of this nonverbal behavior into verbal communications.

THE PATIENT

To illustrate certain manifest changes in emotive soundmaking during psychotherapy, a talkative patient from the psychiatric clinic was invited to participate in psychotherapeutic discussions under the condition that his speech be tape-recorded during each interview. The significance of a patient's agreement to participate in psychotherapy under such conditions cannot be minimized (107). In this case it happened that the patient had serious unresolved oral problems which affected, among other things, the manner in which the recording microphone was incorporated into his fantasies (see Interview 3-9-60).

> The patient is a twenty-six year old unemployed salesman, seeking psychiatric help at a time in life when he needs suddenly to adjust to a new way of living. His wife has recently divorced him, and he has moved into a YMCA hotel where his latent homosexual interests are being excessively stimulated. He is on the verge of an acute depression and attempts to allay his loneliness through aggressive behavior or flight into activity. From doctors he seeks understanding and sympathy by calling attention to a variety of bodily symptoms.

> The patient is the youngest of four children from a conservative New England family that has been on the rise socio-economically. His mother is a hypochrondriacal woman who has been hospitalized and treated somatically for depressions. His father is a powerful banker with considerable political finesse who uses his success

to impress others. He ambivalently offers the patient money to return home and set himself up in business while at the same time telling him to enter a local psychiatric hospital for treatment. In spite of his incipient depression, the patient struggles doggedly to remain independent and get a job on his own.

Since adolescence this man has been a boyish, friendly person, eager to please and afraid of competition. A nice appearance, cleanliness, and ingratiating social manners enabled him to make a good adjustment throughout prep school. But in the Army there was trouble. He found himself on the verge of panic during inspections and dressing-downs from superiors. He often felt like hitting them or shouting back. To relieve his tensions he took it easy on nights off duty and on weekends. Once in a while he drank too much, and then under the guise of a mild intoxication allowed his latent rage to come to the surface. He would become arrogant, provocative, and sometimes belligerent. He masochistically welcomed punishment and court martials since these measures restrained his unmanageable resentment and at the same time allowed him to enjoy being a "no-good bum" until his release from duty. After this he married a foreign-born girl whom he had known for only a few weeks.

Marriage was simultaneously a continuation of this unhappy military career and an attempt to build a new life for himself. The early months of the relationship were spent in an alcoholic haze until a pregnancy forced him to sober up and try to be a man. In various sales jobs, the anxieties about competition reasserted themselves. He felt chronically uneasy, restless, and had vage homosexual fantasies. In the absence of actual showdowns as there had been in the Army, the patient picked fights with his wife. He ridiculed her in front of friends, made fun of her pregnancy, and gave her little emotional support during and after the delivery. After the birth of the baby she decided to call it quits. He submitted to this decision without a whimper, but after the divorce broke down with the symptoms that brought him to the psychiatrist.

When the patient first called on the telephone for an appointment, he sounded tearful, agitated, rather puny, and insubstantial. Furthermore, his soundmaking had a markedly effeminate quality: the voice seemed to mince and waver, much like the swishy, theatrical gestures of certain overt homosexuals. During the period of clinical evaluation, these therapeutic goals were discussed: prevent more depression; keep him from slipping into a more regressed and dependent adjustment; and help him get back on his feet economically.

Therapy was carried out under the supervision of a psychoanalyst who once a week discussed the clinical material and listened to selected samples of the tape-recordings. From the beginning of therapy a link seemed apparent between the patient's use of sounds and his emotional attitudes. A strident, querulous, effeminate-sounding, high-pitched soprano voice went with the expression of aggressive feminine impulses toward the doctor. Conversely, in phases of passivity, self-inhibition, and fear, the patient emitted a much softer, flabby, sad-sounding, low-pitched baritone voice. Characteristically, an utterance would begin on an aggressive note, the patient bursting forth with his high soprano, speaking rapidly and plaintively. As soon as this sound got past his lips, he would interrupt himself, either with silence or with a series of noises, coughs, or throat-clearing, and then abruptly switch into a lower-sounding, soft, submissive, baritone voice.

This rapid back-and-forth fluctuation between a high-loud and a low-soft voice occurred not only within sentences; there were times also that the patient sustained one or the other voice for the duration of several sentences, or even during a major part of the interview. During such more sustained periods one could readily use the content of his verbalization as a guide to the emotional meaning of his soundmaking. It became possible for example to link the high-loud voice with themes like resentment at having to assume responsibility and rage at not getting more help. He often used this aggressive sound to wheedle and provoke others into dealing with him as though he were a child and not an adult. The low-soft voice on the other hand was produced in the context of defeatist attitudes and hypochondriacal concerns. He often made this passive sound as an expression of helplessness and to manipulate others to satisfy his desire for advice, guidance or encouragement. Examples of the relationship between the patient's soundmaking and other aspects of his behavior are cited in Table III at the end of this chapter.

EMOTIVE PATTERNS OF SOUNDMAKING

For half-octave band measurement, samples of sound produced by the patient were taken from the beginning and the end of eleven consecutive tape-recorded interviews. Figure 14 illustrates the results. Sounds at the start of interviews are labelled "A" and sounds from the end of interviews are labelled "Z." Two curves appear in each graph, a solid curve to denote the sound at the beginning of each sentence or utterance, and a dotted curve to denote the sound at its termination. For example, at the start of interview No. 1 on March 2, the patient says: *"putting conversations and things into a negative—b—uh—course or viewpoint."* Half-octave band measurement of the initial segment is represented by the solid curve, a robust voice with motants 1 and 2 fused and motant 3 focussed at 1,430 cps. The terminal segment is represented by the dotted curve, a flat voice with motant 1 at 90 cps, motant 2 at 250 cps, motant 3 around 1,000 cps, and motant 4 at 4,000 cps. The two segments are separated by silence "—————" and two embolophrasic noises *"b"* and *"uh."* These interruptions in his speech mark the turning point between the patient's high-loud robust sound and low-soft flat sound. The pattern just described is repeated with little variation in interviews 3-2-60 (Z), 3-15-60 (A), 3-28-60 (Z), 3-29-60 (A), 3-31-60 (Z), and 4-4-60 (A).

Figure 14 also shows changes in this pattern: for example, at the end of the fourth interview, 3-9-60, two robust curves indicating high-loud voice overlap. The opening statement (solid curve) *"but then eh as I say even—even things that I want to do"* is uttered in an excitable manner, with an aggressive high-pitched tone of voice. This quality is then maintained throughout the terminal statement (dotted curve) *"or that seems enjoyable to me, or I'm looking forward to, I can't even get there on time."* This statement is uttered even more loudly than the opening one, and there is slightly less nasality and a somewhat lower-pitched fundamental tone. This pattern, the persistence of an intense robust sound, occurred in association with a significant shift in the patient's behavior toward the therapist, *viz.*, an increase of rebellious acting-out in the transference. The patient had showed up late for this particular interview terminating with the doubly-ro-

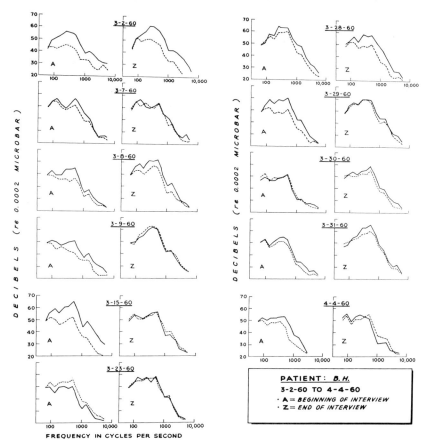

Fig. 14. Half-octave band measurements of sound emitted by a patient at the beginning and end of eleven consecutive psychotherapeutic interviews. Solid curves denote the start of sentences; dashed durves denote the termination.

bust-voice pattern. There were angry gestures and grimaces as he complained bitterly about a dentist who had recently worked on his teeth. He verbalized envy of this man who, unlike the patient, has a schedule for each day and a purpose in life. He also directed a specific complaint against the dentist for putting a mask over his face while drilling.

The therapist correctly took these complaints and expressions of resentment to refer to the psychotherapy itself, since the treatment contract involved the patient's allowing a microphone to be placed in front of his face. The therapist also knew that during the week the patient had been struggling more than ever to resist the direct expression of passive homosexual masochistic desires which treatment had in part stimulated. After this crisis the patient broke two appointments, and during the interval he negotiated an important business deal in which he would passively benefit from the enterprising activities of another man. At the start of the very next treatment interview, 3-15-60 (A), the effeminate voice pattern was back in full force, with its characteristic quick fluctuation between an annoying, screechy, soprano voice and a depressed, clumsy, baritone.

After several further treatment interviews which focussed primarily on the relationship between the patient's feelings of guilt and his inability to hold a steady job, he accepted a position with a company in Hawaii. His mood improved and he left for the trip feeling optimistic about the future. Table III condenses the eleven interviews illustrated acoustically in Figure 14 in order to demonstrate interrelationships between the patient's soundmaking, the content of his verbalizations, and his overall behavior pattern.

What further conclusions can be drawn about the role that analysis of his soundmaking may have played in this patient's treatment? As stated earlier, his particularly intense oral needs which were not being fulfilled outside of therapy undoubtedly influenced what happened in the course of treatment. One may surmise that putting a microphone directly in front of this patient's mouth and focussing so much attention on his acoustic behavior might have had the effects both of bringing oral problems more deliberately into the patient's consciousness and of increasing his sense of frustration over being orally deprived. Furthermore, it became increasingly clear during the course of therapy that the fluctuating character of this patient's emotive soundmaking bore more than an indirect relationship to his internal attitudes, particularly in regard to problems of masculinity — femininity, aggressivity — passivity, and autonomy — dependence. Ferenczi, who observed a similar pattern of emotive soundmaking in a male patient, actually explained this in terms of partial parent identifications; the high-loud soprano voice represented an incomplete introject of the mother and the low-soft baritone the partly introjected father (39). Unfortunately the patient described here left therapy before exploration of deeper psychic processes could be pursued.

TABLE III

A Patient's Behavior During Psychotherapy (See Fig. 14)

Acoustic Pattern	Verbal Content	Behavior Pattern
3-2-60		
There is some increase of sound intensity during the interview. The 250 cps peak of the robust voice in segment Z is 6 decibels higher than that in segment A, but the fluctuating, effeminate-sounding pattern persists throughout the interview.	A: "Putting conversations and things into a negative — b — uh — course or viewpoint." Z: "In talking with you and talking with Miss Smith — re — thirty then to tomorrow all right."	He sizes up the therapist and tries to get approval and guidance. He talks of his friends and how they have failed him. He discusses books about psychiatry he has read. He complains of feeling cold and alone.
3-7-60		
There is a decided reduction of intensity from the previous visit affecting particularly his opening statements. These are now uttered with a sharp-to-flat voice instead of the robust voice. Little change occurs during the interview.	A: "I got a cold — it always wanted — the cold doesn't last very long in itself but the cough — seems to linger on." Z: "People that — suppose this goes along with the — with the fact that I've been that."	He tries to relate to the doctor by being really sick. A cold with a cough has developed since the last interview, and looks terrible. He describes himself as nervous and wonders whether he was "just born lazy." He wonders how therapy can help him and asks for a physical examination.
3-8-60		
The fluctuating pattern is back, and he picks up 7 decibels in motant 2 of the opening statement during the interview. At the end of the hour the closing statement is more robust, and its peak at 500 cps has gone up 9 decibels.	A: "I had an interview yesterday for a job—but —ah—I received this application in the mail last week." Z: "He treated her like a — ah — like a woman which I didn't."	He is boisterous and brags about a sexual conquest the previous night. He talks of his work interests, focussing on "doing things with my hands." He blocks often and says he's embarrassed just like the way he feels when with friends.

3-9-60

At the beginning of the interview, both samples are flat, though there is the characteristic fluctuation between opening and closing statements. At the end of the interview the voice is persistently fixed in the robust voice (see explanation on page 88).	A: "Just a splitting headache, I've been in the dentist's chair since 9 o'clock this morning — (coughing) — pretty punk." Z: "But then eh as I say even — even things that I want to do — or that seem enjoyable to me, or I'm looking forward to, I can't even get there on time."	He is late for the interview and angrily complains about a visit to his dentist. He talks of a friend's suicide and about another friend who was murdered by a gang of negro teenagers. He keeps scratching his head, sniffs, coughs and asks for aspirin. (see explanation on page 88).

3-15-60

At the beginning of the interview the soprano voice reaches 65 decibels at 500 cps. The typical drop to a flat baritone follows. At the end of the interview both samples give the same flat acoustic picture, though intensity is 57 decibels in the half-octave band centered at 500 cps.	A: "And yesterday I just — ah — I called once and didn't get a-hold of you and I didn't call again." Z: "The big complaint he had about me was that I didn't get there on time in the morning and I'm still."	After missing two appointments without explanation, he proudly discloses that he's felt better and "socialized" over the weekend. Actually he acted-out his dependency on his father by calling home and asking his father for help. He had a dream about "the devil." As he talks about his father's bossiness he gets more depressed during the interview.

3-23-60

In this interview there is a reversal of the usual fluctuating pattern. This time the baritone voice comes first and is followed by the high-pitched sound. At the beginning of the interview the soprano is 6 decibels more intense than the baritone at 500 cps. At the end both samples have about the same sound intensity.	A: "I could get up at eight if I — there were just some way to get out of bed." Z: "Well now here again I don't understand because — it's never occurred to me that way."	He overslept and is 20 minutes late for the interview. He has been in various bars over the weekend, talking mainly with older men and soldiers. His father was away in the Army during World War II, and homosexual pre-occupations began at that time. He does not want to be a homosexual.

3-28-60

At the beginning both samples are loud. The high voice reaches 64 decibels at 250 cps and 63 decibels at 500 cps. The fluctuation is again present. This pattern persists throughout the interview, and while not so loud, his effeminate voice is very much in evidence at the close.	A: "You're not sure because of my not showing up — or my showing lately late or what." Z: "I'm going to have to borrow some money from my father this week — I don't know why I said that just now."	He is again twenty minutes late, acts very feminine and provocative. Ambivalently he shakes his head while making positive statements. He worries about losing his job and also about losing the therapist through his acting-out.

3-29-60

Within the interview there is a dramatic change. The fluctuating voice at the beginning pulls together into a steady highpitched robust sound at the end. Except for the flat baritone sample at the beginning, all samples have good intensity levels with maxima of 60 decibels.	A: "The car went out on me — uhum — last night and I had to take the bus up and so." Z: "The idea that comes to my mind that — that — with most people it would be their parents."	He shows some insight into the feminine exhibitionistic quality of his behavior. His ex-wife has a lover now and he is very jealous of them. He thinks much about the man and compares himself unfavorably in terms of physical attributes. He is bothered by an intense itch of the head and wants to scratch his scalp all the time.

3-30-60

The voice at the beginning of the interview is fixed in the flat position. Intensity is low (51 decibels at 500 cps) and there is no fluctuation. At the close of the interview intensity levels are higher (maximum of 59 decibels at 500 cps) and both samples approach a more robust voice.	A: "It's just a way of — saying it I guess." Z: "There's still a good chance that I'm not but — but I — I'm not so sure myself anymore that I'm not."	He feels anxious and restless after visiting his ex-wife in order to meet her lover. He realizes that he wants something more than therapy, maybe "sympathy."

3-31-60

While both at the beginning and at the end of the interview there is fluctuation between the initial and terminal statements in terms of their acoustic analysis, there is now less of a discrepancy between consecutive samples, i.e., A shows two flat voices, Z shows two robust voices. The rise of intensity during the interview is striking — 12 decibels at 500 cps in the high samples.	A: "Well, I'm sure it has serious undertones but it was — a, uh — a little funny to me too when I look back on it." Z: "Before, before we split up — aa — ah, oh the I — I didn't talk with her very often."	He appears overactive and elated, jokes and kids around; flippantly debating some explanations about his childishness that had been offered in previous interviews. He argues about the efficacy of therapy and seems to be more conscious of a conflict about coming to the clinic.

4-4-60

This time, there is little variation in his sound throughout the interview. While some fluctuation persists, the overall pattern is one of flatness. Intensity levels do not get above the 55 decibel level in the half-octave band centered at 500 cps.	A: "Very little happened over the — over the weekend." Z: "It isn't the manly thing to do — uh to — to cry I guess."	He is late again and complains once more about the therapist's lack of "warmth" and unwillingness to respond. His ex-wife and her lover are leaving town, and he feels abandoned. He wants to cry but can't. When asked about the effects of suppressed crying on his voice, he becomes momentarily deaf.

Many features of this patient's psychopathology served to impede recognition of unconscious dynamics: there was, first of all, a facade of pseudomasculinity, belligerence, and aggressivity, which had gotten him into trouble in the Army and had only recently broken down under the stress of his failing marriage. Then there came, during the second phase of his treatment, an attempt to retrench behind a facade of pseudofemininity. The effeminate soundmaking might be considered an acoustic component of this defense, which also became symptomatic in terms of conscious homosexual preoccupations during interviews.

Of additional interest from an acoustic point of view is the efflorescence during psychotherapy of the patient's second motant, thereby jamming sound energy into the frequency band at 500 cps. The persistence of the patient's high-loud robust soprano voice in interview 3-9-60 was particularly striking in this regard. Retrospectively this may be taken to represent an acoustic cue emitted probably unconsciously as a way to directly express craving needs for warmth, affection, and mothering. Whenever the patient could verbalize his desire to cry (and reasons for not giving in to it), his voice lost much of the strident, high-pitched quality denoted acoustically by the robust voice patterns. As already mentioned, the analyses on 4-4-60 showed a predominantly flat, low-pitched, low-intensity pattern, and his voice at that time was full of sadness and resignation. One may surmise from this that once the patient became more consciously aware of his desire to relate anaclitically to the therapist and found the courage to talk about this, his tendency for expressing the desire through emotive soundmaking began to wane.

SUMMARY

In this chapter we control for the effects of individual variability in soundmaking by focussing on the acoustic emissions of one single individual. This is a psychiatric patient whose history, psychopathology, and behavior during psychotherapy is described. Samples of his spontaneous soundmaking at the beginning and the end of each of eleven interviews are measured acoustically. The results tend to bear out an earlier observation made by psychotherapists, viz. that fluctuations in the intensity-frequency characteristics of soundmaking among patients are related to how they externalize different psychic introjects. Further acoustic research is needed to clarify this point. In addition, the clinical material presented here suggests that during many interviews the patient suppressed a desire to cry. I propose that this partly unconscious defense against the expression of passive, anaclitic impulses directed towards the therapist also may account for this patient's frequently high-pitched, strident soundmaking.

Chapter 8

ACOUSTIC VARIABILITY —
TWO GROUPS OF SOUNDMAKERS

The preceding chapter presented acoustic measurements of sound emitted by a patient in the course of psychotherapy. We noted that when this man made aggressive demands upon his therapist, analysis of his voice revealed a more robust pattern than when he was passive and resigned, in which case the voice was flat and less intense. Moreover it seemed as though he would jam acoustic energy into the half-octave band centered at 500 cps—the second motant—as if to say (non-verbally) "look here, I'm like a baby, I need help." It was suggested that this form of soundmaking represents a kind of emotional expression, an activity which can substitute for verbal behavior at times when patients cannot deal denotatively with their personal problems.

To lend credence to such a hypothesis we must have additional information about human soundmaking. We need to know, first of all, whether acoustic measurement of sounds emitted by other persons besides the particular patient presented in Chapter 7 reveals any systematic variability in the pattern of soundmaking. Furthermore we shall have to find out whether such patterns of acoustic variability relate significantly to any variables pertaining to the emotional life of the soundmakers in question. For this reason two groups of soundmakers were studied. One group of twenty nonpatients was exposed to an emotionally stressful situation and the sounds they made before and after the stress were measured and compared. Another group—thirty emotionally disturbed psychiatric patients—was studied before and after treatment so as to compare changes of soundmaking in terms of psychopathology, type of treatment, symptomatic recovery, and other clinical variables.

TWENTY PERSONS UNDER STRESS

To study the pattern of acoustic variability as related to an emotionally stressful situation, we randomly selected twenty persons from the working population of the Medical Center. Most of the subjects were professionals (physicians, chemists, nurses, psychologists) while two were semi-skilled workers from the maintenance staff. The group was about equally divided as to sex—nine men and eleven women—and the age spread was from twenty-two to fifty years, with an average of thirty-three years. The subjects were invited individually to participate in an experiment, the declared purpose of which was to study changes in their soundmaking.

Procedure

The standard setup for tape-recording and for acoustic analysis of the tapes was used. To minimize the suggestive influence of the experimenter's voice on the soundmaking of the subjects, instructions for the experiment were printed on cards given to each subject as he took his seat behind the microphone. On a small table nearby stood a glass about half-filled with a clear liquid. This was a solution of ammonium chloride, a liquid with a vile and irritating smell.

Each subject was instructed to do the following:

1. Pick up the glass on the table in front of you and put it directly under your nose. Take a full breath and say the following sentence three times:

JOE TOOK FATHER'S SHOE BENCH OUT
JOE TOOK FATHER'S SHOE BENCH OUT
JOE TOOK FATHER'S SHOE BENCH OUT

2. Put the glass down. Breathe normally three or four times. Again take a full breath and say:

JOE TOOK FATHER'S SHOE BENCH OUT
JOE TOOK FATHER'S SHOE BENCH OUT
JOE TOOK FATHER'S SHOE BENCH OUT*

Half the group was given instruction cards on which these directions were interchanged, so that the first step of the experiment was non-stressful while the second step involved exposure

---

* These sample verbal statements are taken from Fletcher's book *Speech and Hearing in Communication* (42). The sentence, "Joe took father's shoe bench out," has been used for many years in experiments on speech acoustics. Together with "she was waiting at my lawn," this nonsense contain all English phonemes that contribute appreciably to the loudness of speech.

to the olfactory stimulus. This was necessary to rule out the effects of presentation order on the soundmaking behavior of the group.

As a psychiatrist unfamiliar with the technical problems of experimental psychology, I was amazed to observe how difficult it is for subjects actually to carry out apparently simple directions required for a scientific experiment. Several subjects simply sat in the chair and did nothing until I pointed repeatedly to the card of instructions. Apparently acoustic directives more effectively initiate behavior under certain conditions—in this case soundmaking in a strange laboratory—than do visual cues. After overcoming their initial reluctance to participate in the experiment, some subjects displayed a tremendous amount of kinesic activity in addition to soundmaking. For example, one subject suddenly stood up, climbed onto the chair, turned around in a full circle, squatted in the chair for a moment, then climbed down and sat normally. Both of us were amused at this incident, and also rather embarrassed because here, in the setting of an apparently orderly and "controlled" experimental procedure, a supposedly "normal" person had suddenly engaged in symbolic behavior which under other circumstances might be considered psychopathologic. This experimental subject was evidently responding to some instructions not contained on the card put in front of him. Another person became quite suspicious and performed the routine extremely slowly as though catatonic, very carefully pondering each step of the instructions as he proceeded.*

Processing the Acoustic Data

Samples were cut from the twenty master tapes and made into tape-loops for acoustic measurement. The second of each set of sentences was selected for analysis, since this sample seemed minimally distorted by the effects upon the subjects of starting

---

* I don't know how often such things happen in test procedures carried out by more experienced experimentalists. One almost never sees them reported in the psychological literature. This is too bad, because such individualized responses may help one evaluate both the results and the lack of results of a specific procedure. Idiosyncratic behavior in the face of specific experimental instructions should also make one question the validity of conclusions based on statistical analysis of the results of the experiment.

and then stopping to speak. Most of the subjects emitted the three sample sentences in a single breath; thus selection of the second sentence eliminated the onset and end of exhalation.

Acoustic energy-levels for each half-octave band of the frequency spectrum between 53 cps and 6,800 cps were measured with the H. H. Scott Sound Analyzer. This resulted in fourteen measurements for each sample of sound. The total intensity of each sample was also measured and used as a baseline for comparing stress and non-stress samples with each other.*

Statistical Analysis of the Data

Nonparametric methods were used to compare the results of acoustic measurement during stress and non-stress situations (118). The question for statistical evaluation was: *Given a set of difference scores in decibels re overall intensity levels) that represent intensity levels A minus intensity levels B for particular half-octave bands between 53 cps and 6,800 cps, could this set have been selected from a population of scores with a mean of zero?* The Signed Rank Test for Paired Observations was applied twice, 1) to determine the effect of olfactory stress on the acoustic measurements, and 2) to determine the effect of presentation order on the acoustic measurements.

Results

1) *The Effect of Olfactory Stress:*

In this test, intensity levels A represented samples of sound recorded after the subjects had smelled the concentrated ammonia solution, and intensity levels B represented samples recorded after the subjects had not whiffed the bad smell. The results are shown in Table IV. Of the fourteen half-octave band

---

*Comparisons made on the basis of the arbitrary intensity of 0 decibels would be meaningless, since this assumes the individual half-octave band levels to be independent variables, which they are not. Due to the presence of resonance energy-peaks (motants), a change in one half-octave band may be related to a change in another band. For example, as intensity rises in the 425 to 600 cps band, it may simultaneously fall in the 600 to 850 cps band. Total intensity levels on the other hand reflect the way acoustic energy is distributed across the individual spectrum analyses and therefore give better baselines for comparative study.

TABLE IV

ACOUSTIC CHANGES RELATED TO AN OLFACTORY STRESS

Subject	53–75	75–106	106–150	150–212*	212–300	300–425	425–600*	600–850	850–1200	1200–1700	1700–2400	2400–3400	3400–4800	4800–6800	Total Intensiy
1	0	-1	-1	0	-2	0	2	1	1	1	2	2	1	1	0
2	0	2	2	2	1	0	1	-3	-2	-1	0	-2	-2	0	1
3	1	0	1	1	0	1	2	0	-3	1	-2	1	0	0	2
4	2	-1	0	0	-2	-1	2	0	-1	-1	-2	0	1	0	1
5	-2	-1	0	2	0	-1	0	-1	0	-1	0	0	0	-2	-1
6	-2	-2	-1	-2	2	3	3	1	-1	0	0	2	-2	-3	1
7	2	3	2	3	1	1	1	-2	-2	-2	-1	0	5	2	2
8	2	2	0	1	0	0	-1	-3	-3	-2	-1	-2	3	1	1
9	0	-1	0	0	1	0	0	-1	-1	-1	2	4	-2	0	-1
10	-1	-1	0	1	0	-2	1	2	-1	-1	4	3	3	4	2
11	-2	-3	-1	0	0	0	-1	-2	2	-1	3	3	4	4	-1
12	0	0	2	0	-1	0	4	-1	1	0	-2	-2	-1	-1	0
13	3	3	0	1	2	-1	1	-1	0	0	2	5	0	0	3
14	-1	-1	0	0	-2	1	1	0	0	-3	1	1	-1	-2	-1
15	-1	0	-1	-1	-1	1	0	0	0	1	0	0	-1	-1	0
16	-2	1	0	0	0	1	-1	-1	3	-2	-1	-1	-1	0	0
17	0	0	2	2	1	0	0	-1	0	1	0	-1	1	-2	0
18	-2	-1	0	0	-1	1	-1	2	2	-2	-1	1	1	0	1
19	2	-1	-2	-2	1	-1	0	3	2	0	-3	-2	-2	-1	-3
20	-1	-1	-1	-1	0	2	0	0	2	1	2	2	2	1	0

*Significant at the 5 percent level of confidence

Difference scores (in decibels re total intensity levels) between two sets of Acoustic Measurements intensity levels tested, two revealed statistically significant changes (p $\leqslant$ .05): these were the 106-150 cps half-octave band (centered at 125 cps) and the 425-600 cps half-octave band (centered at 500 cps). In both bands the difference was in the direction of lower intensity levels under stressful condition.

2) *The Effect of Presentation Order:*

In this test, intensity levels A represented samples of sound recorded the first time the subject uttered "Joe took father's shoe bench out," and intensity levels B represented samples of the second recording. Changes in one of the half-octave bands were statistically significant at the five percent level. This was the 106-150 cps half-octave band (centered at 125 cps). The difference was in the direction of lower intensity levels for the first recording.

Comments

It is of interest that the two half-octave bands which showed significant intensity changes in the experiment are located in regions of the acoustic frequency spectrum that were earlier called motants; the half-octave band centered at 125 cps overlaps motant 1 and the half-octave band centered at 500 cps overlaps motant 2. While this lends support to the hypothesis about emotive soundmaking, the experiment does not prove that stress was really responsible for producing the change.* We already know that presentation order was significantly associated with an intensity change of motant 1. What about other known variables, for instance sex of the subjects. Perhaps male speakers responded differently to the stress situation than did females.

When the group was divided according to sex (nine males, eleven females) and the Sum of Ranks Test was applied to the difference scores obtained from comparing the fourteen half-octave band levels and the total intensity levels, none of the fifteen tests reached statistical significance at the five per cent

---

* In running 14 tests on data drawn from a population with a mean of zero, one can expect a number of them to be significant by chance. When Poisson's variable was computed, it did not rule out this possibility. Therefore the null-hypothesis cannot be rejected for the series of tests.

level. Other factors such as age, intelligence, education, and physical characteristics of subjects were not studied.

Conclusions

1. Acoustic intensity levels shifted in certain places along the frequency spectrum, apparently as a function of some behavior variable.
2. These shifts involved the first motant when presentation order was the variable under consideration.
3. These shifts involved the first and second motants when olfactory stress was the variable under consideration.

THIRTY PATIENTS BEFORE AND AFTER TREATMENT

A second group of subjects was studied to obtain additional information about measurable changes of soundmaking related to emotional factors. This group consisted of thirty acutely ill psychiatric patients on a hospital treatment ward. Seventeen patients were females and thirteen were males. Their ages ranged from thirteen to seventy-four, with an average of thirty-eight years. Each patient was tape-recorded as soon as possible after admission to obtain before-treatment samples of soundmaking.

Procedure

To obtain a representative sample of each patient's soundmaking during acute emotional illness, more time was allowed for the tape-recording sessions than with the nonpatient group recorded for the stress experiment reported earlier. The purpose of the study was carefully explained to each patient, and in the course of this introductory interview—which in some cases lasted as long as one hour—the following printed paragraph was presented to each patient. He was asked to read this into the recording microphone:

> Joe took father's shoe bench out she was waiting at my lawn Joe took father's shoe bench out she was waiting at my lawn Joe took father's shoe bench out she was waiting at my lawn*

Several of the more confused schizophrenic patients had

---

* See footnote, page 97.

difficulty with this task. One catatonic woman remained mute for forty minutes before she agreed to speak into the microphone. Several patients responded to the absense of punctuation in the sample paragraph by stopping at unexpected places; they then had to be prompted to proceed. A number of patients wanted to impose meaning upon fragments of the paragraph, trying to make sense out of its nonsense. However, in each case sufficient sound-making for acoustic measurement was tape-recorded under both spontaneous and reading conditions.

The fragment "Joe took father's shoe bench out" was made into a tape-loop; whenever possible the second utterance of this phrase was used for the reasons explained in the experimental stress study. This tape fragment—labelled "reading voice"—was run through the half-octave band analyzer, and results were used for statistical comparisons. Particular attention was paid to four points along the frequency spectrum that previous acoustic studies showed to be most indicative of change:

125 cps — the center frequency of the half-octave band 106-150 *cps* — locating motant 1;

500 cps — the center frequency of the half-octave band 425-600 cps — locating motant 2;

1,430 cps — the center frequency of the half-octave band 1,200-1,700 cps — locating motant 3; and

5,700 cps — the center frequency of the half-octave band 4,800-6,800 cps — locating motant 4.

In addition to a statistical study of the reading voice samples, spontaneous speech patterns for each individual patient were sampled and measured. This was done to study changes of pitch and other sound qualities as related to treatment. Tape samples containing high-pitched sound from the interview were labelled "high voice"; those containing low-pitched sound were labelled "low voice." Since these samples came from spontaneous speech, they showed considerable linguistic variability and hence were unsuitable for statistical comparison of acoustic measurements. The spontaneous samples did however provide important insights into patterns of change in soundmaking of the patients and these will be summarized below.

The entire procedure—explanation, tape-recording of spontaneous speech, reading of the standard paragraph, and half-octave band measurement of high voice, low voice, and reading voice—was repeated after a period of time ranging from ten days to two months, and averaging three weeks. During this interval each patient had received psychiatric treatment, and manifest changes in his clinical condition were known to the ward physicians and nurses.

Patterns of Change

Three distinct patterns of change in the acoustic analyses of soundmaking before and after treatment were observed:

1) *Increased Robustness*

This pattern of change is demonstrated by the case of a sixty-four year old salesman who entered the hospital during the depressed phase of a manic-depressive illness. His sound showed a

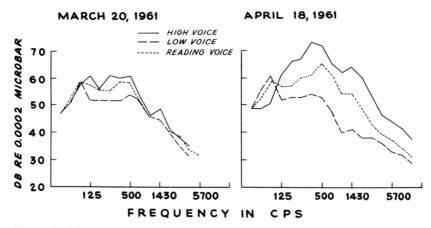

Fig. 15. Changes in the sound of a depressed patient associated with electroconvulsive treatment. Note the increased pattern of robustness after treatment.

predominantly flat pattern when initially analyzed (Fig. 15, March 20, 1961). Of the three samples shown in the figure, the reading voice based on the standard paragraph has motant 1 centered at 90 cps with an intensity level of 59 decibels. Motant 2 also comes to 59 decibels, it has a flat, plateau shape across the octave-region 300 to 600 cps. There is a drop in energy levels above this point, and no clearly defined third or fourth motants are visible. His high voice, used during spontaneous utterances made in anger, has a precise motant centered at 125 cps, at an intensity level of 61 decibels. Motant 2 is biphasic, with both peaks attaining an intensity level also of 61 decibels. Motant 3 is clearly shown as a peak focussed at 1,430 cps. A sample of low voice which characterizes this patient's more apathetic spontaneous statements, has motant 1 again located at 90 cps, 59 decibels in intensity. But in contrast to the other two voices, motant 2 does not match the height of motant 1, it comes only to a small peak in the half-octave band centered at 500 cps.

Two weeks later and after five electroconvulsive treatments, this patient's acoustic analysis showed a strikingly different pattern (Fig. 15, April 18, 1961). His reading voice and his high voice both are now much more robust, in contrast to the earlier flat patterns. The reading voice has motant 1 centered at 90 cps and a prominent 65 decibel motant 2 at 500 cps. The high voice shows a massive concentration of acoustic energy; motants 1 and 2 appear to be fused; they come to 73 decibels in the octave-region 300-600 cps. There is a 64 decibel peak at 1,430 cps for motant 3. Only the low voice sample looks like this man's sound before treatment. It has one prominent peak, motant 1 at 90 cps, and the generally flat-to-hollow configuration of the earlier low voice. This suggests that in spite of his more robust soundmaking after treatment, this patient still has acoustic evidence of depression which would have to be considered in an overall evaluation of his clinical improvement.

2. *Decreased Sharpness*

Another pattern of change associated with treatment is demonstrated by a sixteen year old girl who entered the hospital during an acute schizophrenic state characterized by withdrawal and apathy. The acoustic analysis done on admission showed a predominantly sharp pattern (Fig. 16, March 23, 1961). Of the three samples analyzed, all have motant 1 firmly fixed at around 50 decibels in the half-octave band centered at 180 cps. The reading voice and a sample of low voice—a monotonous sound pervading her speech most of the time—show motant 2 placed exactly one octave higher, also at 50 decibels, giving the typical twin-

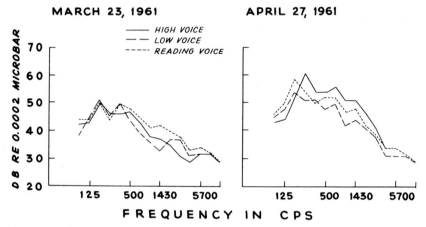

Fig. 16. Changes in the sound of a schizophrenic patient associated with chemotherapy. Note the rise of intensity and decrease of sharpness after treatment.

peak pattern of sharp voices. The high voice, a high-pitched pleading sound, gives the flat pattern, with motant 2 slightly peaked at 500 cps. All three samples show additional regions of energy concentration—for example the reading voice has motant 3 at 1,430 cps and motant 4 at 5,700 cps.

One month later, after the patient had been on phenothiazine drugs (Fig. 16, April 27, 1961) the acoustic pattern lost a good deal of the sharpness seen in the initial analysis. While the low and the reading samples still have motant 1 centered at 180 cps, there is now a five decibel difference between the two peaks. Neither of the two samples have the twin-peak shape characteristic of sharp voice patterns. The low voice sample has motant 2 split in two components, a plateau in octave-region 212 to 425 cps, and a peak at 715 cps. The reading voice sample has a broader single focus of acoustic energy in motant 2, a plateau in the octave-region 425 to 850 cps. Only the high voice sample has some twin-peaking, but not at an octave interval. This sample reaches 61 decibels for motant 1 at 250 cps, certainly a more intense fundamental tone component than this patient produced when she was acutely ill. All three samples of speech sound in after-treatment acoustic measurements also show appreciable concentrations of energy in motant 3 at 1,430 cps.

3. *Increased Uniformity of the Acoustic Curves*

In this pattern of change associated with treatment, the basic acoustic characteristics of the sound remained the same, but the variability between different samples collected during single interviews, became much less. For example: Fig. 17, January 4, 1961, shows the sounds of a thirty-two year old, acutely hypochondriacal female patient at the time of admission to the hospi-

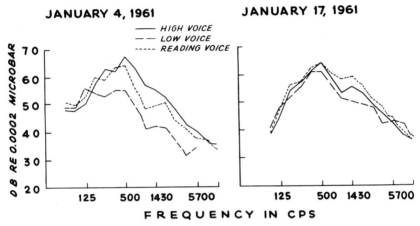

Fig. 17. Changes in the sound of an excited hypochondriacal patient associated with supportive therapy. Note the increased uniformity between high, low, and reading voice after treatment.

tal. She was worried about her symptoms and appeared to be very excited lest she not receive sufficient attention and proper treatment. Her soundmaking alternated rapidly in pitch between a strident high voice and a throaty low one. According to the acoustic measurements shown in Figure 17, the high sound is characterized by a robust voice pattern with motant 1 at 250 cps and motant 2 at 500 cps. The second motant is unusually intense —67 decibels. The low voice is flat; its motant 1 is located at 125 cps, and motant 2 is spread out across the octave-region 300 to 600 cps. The reading voice lies between these two samples, having motant 1 at 180 cps and a rather flat motant 2, with a level of 64 decibels, at 500 cps.

After treatment, acoustic measurement curves of the three samples of soundmaking look much more alike (Fig. 17, January

TABLE V

ACOUSTIC CHANGES ASSOCIATED WITH PSYCHIATRIC TREATMENT

	Clinical Variables					Acoustic Variables					
Pat. No.	Sex A=male B=female	Age A=<20 B=20-50 C=>50	Diagnosis A=psychotic B=non-psychotic	Treatment A=ECT B=no ECT	Outcome A=0 B=+ C=++	Difference scores in: half-octave bands centered at				Difference scores (x 10) for Total* Spectrum	Difference scores for Time-duration in seconds (x 10) for reading sample†
						125 cps	500 cps*	1430 cps	5700 cps		
1	B	A	A	B	A	3	4	6	0	16	-8
2	B	B	A	B	B	1	-1	3		8	-10
3	B	B	B	B	B	0	6	4	-1	12	-3
4	A	B	A	A	C	0	5	0	1	6	8
5	B	B	A	A	B	-1	-4	0	0	-9	-4
6	A	C	A	A	C	-3	0	2	2	1	-2
7	B	B	A	A	C	1	16	12	3	31	-16
8	A	C	A	B	C	4	3	5		1	3
9	B	B	B	A	A	0	22	14	5	43	8
10	A	C	A	A	B	4	33	16	0	39	-2
11	A	B	A	A	B	3	11	7		32	0
12	A	C	A	B	A	3	15	7		42	-12
13	A	A	A	B	A	0	12	13	5	25	-6
14	B	A	B	B	A	-3	2	-3	0	-4	-2
15	A	B	A	B	B	-1	-11	-5	-4	-23	-12
16	A	C	A	A	B	8	4	1	7	15	0
17	A	B	B	A	C	-1	-9	-5	-8	-35	3
18	A	C	A	A	A	-5	15	7		43	-6
19	B	A	B	B	B	0	35	11	9	78	4
20	B	B	B	B	B	9	-9	-13	-1	-44	-2
21	B	B	B	B	A	0	6	3	0	6	-4
22	B	B	B	B	C	1	-5	-2	-3	-12	16
23	B	B	A	B	B	-5	0	2	9	13	-2
24	A	B	A	B	B	-1	-2	0	-1	-7	-2
25	A	C	B	B	C	0	1	1	-1	4	1
26	B	B	A	A	B	4	5	-1		-9	2
27	A	C	B	B	B	1	3	5	3	10	1
28	B	B	B	B	B	3	6	4	0	19	0
29	B	B	A	A	B	3	11	8	3	22	13
30	B	B	B	B	A	3	1	-1	-4	-3	-10

* Significantly related at the 5 percent level to the treatment variable.
† Related (p < 1.0) to the age variable.

17, 1961). Treatment in this case consisted of psychotherapy with a psychiatric resident; no somatic therapy was used. The patient was an intelligent and verbal person who readily came to understand the emotional significance of her somatic symptoms. With reduction of tension and fearfulness, she seemed much more comfortable when the second tape-recording was made. All three samples now have a robust pattern, with prominent concentrations of acoustic energy into the mid-range of the frequency spectrum. Motants 1 and 2 appear to be fused and come to a peak at 500 cps. The high and reading voice samples also show a peak for motant 3 at 1,430 cps. The low voice sample shows motant 4 at 5,700 cps.

Processing the Acoustic Data

As previously mentioned, intensity level changes in the half-octave bands centered at 125, 500, 1,430, and 5,700 cps were compared. Table V shows the results under "acoustic variables." Note that in this study of patients decibel values were converted to sones—units of subjective loudness (126)—for reasons already explained in the footnote on page 99. Another acoustic variable shown in the Table pertains to the time it took to read the sample "Joe took father's shoe bench out she was waiting at my lawn" as measured by stop watch. Before-and-after treatment results in this measure of soundmaking were also compared and the variability was studied statistically.

Processing the Clinical Data

Five clinical variables—sex, age, diagnosis, treatment, and results of treatment—were determined for each of the thirty patients. The data for this is tabulated on Table V under "clinical variables." This tabulation is based on the following groupings of clinical data:

Sex of Patients

Group A — Males (13 patients)
Group B — Females (17 patients)

Age

Group A — Below 20 years (4 patients)

Group B — Between 20 and 50 years (17 patients)
Group C — Over 50 years (9 patients)

Diagnosis*

Group A — Psychotic Reactions (19 patients)
Group B — Nonpsychotic Reactions (11 patients)

Form of Treatment†

Group A — Electroconvulsive Treatment (9 patients)
Group B — No electroconvulsive Treatment (21 patients)

Outcome of Treatment as Rated by Ward Psychiatrists

Group A — 0 (No symptomatic improvement)
(8 patients)
Group B — + (Symptomatic improvement) (16 patients)
Group C — + + (Overall improvement) (6 patients)

Statistical Analysis of the Data

Nonparametric methods were used. The overall question to which tests of statistical hypothesis were directed was: *Are there any significant relationships between 1) a set of difference scores for soundmaking before and after treatment and 2) a tabulation of five clinical variables?* The Sum of Ranks Test was used to answer this question for loudness changes in the four half-octave bands chosen to represent motants 1, 2, 3, and 4, for total loudness changes, and for time-duration changes.‡

Results

1) The relationship between clinical variables and loudness changes in half-octave bands chosen to represent motants 1, 2, 3, and 4:

---

* The diagnostic classifications of psychiatric disorders officially approved by the American Psychiatric Association was used (23).

† Since all patients received hospital care, occupational and recreational therapy, psychotherapy, and in many cases various medications, only the use of electroconvulsive treatment in the course of hospitalization was taken as criterion for this variable.

‡ The Mann-Whitney U Test was used when there were 2 groups in the clinical classifications, and the Kruskal-Wallis Test was used when the number of groups was 3.

Loudness changes of motant 2, represented by the 425-600 cps half-octave band (centered at 500 cps) were significantly related to variable 4, the form of treatment ($p \leq .05$). The nine patients who received electroconvulsive treatment showed a significant trend towards loudness increases (equivalent to a *rise* in acoustic energy) at 500 cps. The twenty-one patients who did not receive electroconvulsive treatment failed to show this trend—they tended instead to show either no loudness changes or loudness decreases at 500 cps.

2) The relationship between clinical variables and changes in total loudness:

Again a significant relationship ($p \leq .05$) was found to exist between overall loudness changes (total of all the half-octave bands measured) and variable 4, the form of treatment. As in the case of the half-octave band centered at 500 cps, total loudness levels increased among the patients receiving electroconvulsive treatment and either did not change or decreased in the nonelectroconvulsive treatment group.

3) The relationship between clinical variables and time-duration of the reading samples:

There was a strong trend towards statistical significance ($p < 1.0$) in the test of this relationship insofar as the age variable was concerned. The greatest speedup in the time it took to read "Joe took father's shoe bench out she was waiting at my lawn" was among the four patients who were less than twenty years old and the younger patients in the twenty to fifty year age group. Conversely, the older patients tended to show no change in the speed of their reading, or became slower when the after-treatment sample was compared with the before-treatment sample.

Comments

It is not too surprising that two of the five clinical variables, diagnosis and results of treatment, were not systematically related to any acoustic changes. Both of these variables are based on judgments of psychopathology. It may well be that at the present time our psychiatric nomenclature does not adequately describe subtle changes in psychopathology over time (143), particularly those subtleties which might influence such fine-grained diagnostic criteria as acoustic measurements.

But what about the first variable, sex of the patient? This is a pretty objective criterion, according to most texts on soundmaking, which state quite categorically that males sound different than females (71). Why did this study show no significant relationships between acoustic changes and sex of the patients? One could blame the method were it not for the fact that two clinical variables *did* correlate significantly. Perhaps some notions about human soundmaking need to be revised: is it possible that sociocultural demands may override the effects of innate anatomic and physiologic factors in soundmaking when it comes to so complex a behavior as the acoustic portrayal of gender? Perhaps the absence of correlation between sex and soundmaking among psychiatric patients is a reflection of the confusion in sexual identification found not infrequently among emotionally disturbed persons (45).

Another item worth comment is the finding here—as in the stress experiment—of a significant change in soundmaking located at the 500 cps point of the frequency spectrum. Spectrographic studies of speech also show significant energy foci here, called the first formant (42). We have deliberately called attention to energy foci below this point—see Chapters 5 and 6—specifically a first motant indicating the laryngeal fundamental—and we used the term second motant to refer to resonance energy around 500 cps. It now seems that there may be a tie-up between what phoneticians call the first formant and what acoustic study labels motant 2. This possible link warrants further investigation.

Conclusions

1) A change in the loudness of soundmaking by psychiatric patients was the single most reliable acoustic criterion of clinical change. It correlated significantly with an objective clinical variable, *viz.*, the use of electroconvulsive treatment.

2) That portion of the acoustic frequency spectrum which

we have called motant 2 (centered at 500 cps) was the only point of energy concentration along the spectrum which changed significantly in association with a clinical variable (Form of Treatment.)

3) A change in time-duration was also a reliable acoustic variable; the younger patients tended to speed up, while the older patients tended to slow down in their soundmaking measured before and after treatment.

SUMMARY

A more systematic attempt to relate acoustic and behavioral variables in soundmaking is presented in this chapter. Individual variability is controlled by studying groups of soundmakers and applying statistical methods. Linguistic variability is controlled by having all subjects read a standard sentence. Twenty non-patient volunteers were put under stress, and their sounds emitted before and after the experience were measured. Significant energy fluctuations occurred in two out of fourteen adjacent half-octave bands. Samples studied after the stress experience showed a reduction of acoustic energy levels at 500 cps, suggesting a suppression of soundmaking. Thirty hospitalized psychiatric patients were next studied. Sound samples were obtained before and after treatment (electroshock, drugs, and psychotherapy). Changes in the half-octave band patterns are described. Of the four bands tested with statistical methods, the one centered at 500 cps again fluctuated significantly. Patients who had received electroshock manifested elevations in acoustic energy levels at this point and in their total energy output, suggesting that an inhibition of soundmaking had been removed. Changes in time-duration of soundmaking were also noted, younger patients tending to speed up their reading after treatment, and older patients tending to slow down. These studies confirm, I believe, that there are significant relationships between soundmaking and psychopathology, and that these relationships can be defined scientifically.

Chapter 9

LISTENER RESPONSES TO BABY SOUNDS

The acoustic findings of preceding chapters very strongly suggest that one characteristic of emotive soundmaking may be its similarity to certain preverbal sounds of infancy. It was found that under stress and in settings of emotional illness, soundmakers tend to become louder and tend to concentrate acoustic energy at 500 cps — in the same half-octave band where the fundamental tone of the baby cry is located.

While much more evidence is needed to prove that alarm sounds among human adults are analogous to certain infantile noises, it behooves us at this time to also pay attention to listeners, since without them there could be no acoustic communication of emotion whatsoever (4). Unless one can show that listeners respond readily to the kinds of sounds we have been describing, and that such responses are strongly emotional, no further acoustic studies of emotive soundmaking would be convincing, or even necessary. Some spontaneous reactions of secretaries who accidentally overheard tape-recorded baby cries were mentioned in Chapter 4. Now more systematic studies of listener responses to artificial (recorded) baby sounds will be presented.

THE WILMER TEST

In 1951, Dr. Harry Wilmer reported the use of an auditory projective test made up of twenty-one pre-recorded acoustic stimuli, each less than one minute in duration and consisting of various human sounds and mechanical noises. These sounds are presented to individuals or groups of listeners who are to verbalize their thoughts and describe their feelings after listening to each stimulus, much like subjects who have been stimulated visually with the Thematic-Apperception Test (140).

Two of the twenty-one acoustic stimuli in the Wilmer Test include baby sounds: *Stimulus Sound #3*, lasting thirty-four seconds, has one baby crying loudly, with a fundamental pitch fluctuating between 320 and 440 cps. In the background are noises of seagulls (about 1,400 cps), plus some more distant baby cry sounds. Close to the end of the recording there is a cough, apparently produced by the same baby which has been crying. *Stimulus Sound # 14* lasts fifty-two seconds. It consists of shrill baby cries and screams, accompanied by a woman vocalizing Brahms' Lullaby and several times trying to shush the baby.

In using the Wilmer Test diagnostically, one presents all twenty-one stimulus sounds consecutively, notes reaction-times to the different noises, and collects any verbal and behavioral responses of the listener for later interpretation. For our purpose here, only listener reactions to Sounds #3 and #14—those featuring baby sounds—are presented.

Patient 1.

The listener is a thirty-nine year old married cashier who became partially blind following a heart operation. Previously an active, independent man who assumed more than his share of responsibility, he now is quite helpless and cannot care for himself. He characterizes himself as a "stumblebum." His wife is crippled, has her hands full with two young children, and cannot effectively assist her husband with his handicap. Being a proud person who does not easily acknowledge helplessness, the patient denies all problems other than blindness, and demands that his sight be fully restored.

Response to Sound #3: "I don't know why, but it seems to me that the scene is in a duckblind, I don't know whether that's the sound of the baby or the sound of the duckcall. I've never heard either one, I shouldn't say either one, but, this there's the sound of birds in the distance, so I associate that with the fact that they're possibly hunters, or, trying to imitate the sound of birds, or, it also sounds like the cry of a baby." (Well, what would a baby be doing in a duckblind?) "If I take the approach that it's a duckblind then I would say that these hunters are in a field and there are birds flying back and forth, and the hunters are blowing on this whistle thing to coax the birds closer to them, and that's about it."

Response to Sound #14: (patient smiles and winces while listening to this sound.) "The mother is in a nursery, the baby is in the crib, and she's trying to rock the baby to sleep. — She's very happy and -ah- she's singing to the baby — a lullaby — I get the sense of complete happiness and relaxed contentment, love, affection, and can see the, feel the love for the baby that's in the crib. I can almost feel the mother, the child, the crib, the room, I can't picture it, but I can feel it. Peace, peace of mind — all complete contentment."

Interpretation: While the patient correctly perceives the baby sounds in both stimuli, his response to Sound #3 is characterized by confusion and denial. It is overdetermined by self-pity (duckblind), suspiciousness (imitation of sounds), and hostility (hunters). Not until hearing Sound #14 where maternal sounds are also audible does he acknowledge anaclitic, tender, peaceful aspects of care-taking and more openly express interest in what he wants (peace, complete contentment).

Patient 2.

This patient was admitted to the hospital at age seventy. Unmarried, she lives alone and has become increasingly isolated socially. Recently she called the police after an angry argument with her neighbors. Clinically she is paranoid, somewhat hard-of-hearing, and in mild cardiac failure. Throughout life she has been a bossy, dominating person, self-supporting and headstrong. Emotionally she is attached to an older sister, whose recent death precipitated severe feelings of loneliness, helplessness, and depression. Following each acoustic stimulus from the Wilmer Test, the patient verbalized profusely and angrily.

Response to Sound #3: "Confusion—but the reason, I wouldn't have any idea in this world—no hint, not any idea possible—the cause? Absolutely nothing I'd be familiar with—not a word" (recognize any sound?) "I heard a sound, but it didn't mean a thing to me—definite confusion—but what caused the confusion, I haven't a lead, no. Sounded like something very, very urgent, needed attention, but not from me, I would not know what it was all about. I've never been called on to participate in something of that nature—positively no."

Response to Sound #14: "Another wild woman shrieking."

(She imitates the cries of the baby, with good tonal accuracy.) "That's what I'm hearing. Sounds like the lamentations of somebody. Jeremiah, I guess. Some woman singing. A sweet voice trying to sing."

Interpretation: The entire listening experience—confinement, confrontation with sounds, and discussion of her fantasies—was deeply disturbing to this patient. Her desperate denial points at the intensity of feelings about what she heard. She mentions the urgency of the sound and that it calls for attention, but poignantly adds "but not from me," thus acknowledging her lack of fulfillment as a woman. Sound #14 reminded her indirectly of herself —a wild woman screaming—and she even imitated the baby sounds. It is of interest that several nights after the Wilmer Test was done this patient reported she heard "the screechy voice of death" calling her name in the darkness.

Patient 3.

This listener is a twenty year old laborer who was severely injured in a motorcycle crash. For months he was comatose, then aphasic, and now has a residual hemiplegia. He is easily annoyed, and his speech and movements are generally stiff and overcontrolled. He is unable to get a job, and psychiatric evaluation was requested to see if anything can be done to help ease his irritability, sense of inadequacy, and passivity.

Response to Sound #3: "Nursery, harumph, nursery in a hospital, babies."

Response to Sound #14: "Mother and a baby. (?) How my family would be if I were married and had a child. How would she treat him, or her, the child in either case."

Interpretation: While sparse, abrupt, and angry, these responses nevertheless reveal something of the preoccupations underlying this patient's mood. He places the baby sounds in the hospital, where he would like to be. Sound #14 stimulates his concern about the future, and raises the question of sexual confusion (him or her) in connection with marriage and parenthood.

Patient 4.

This is the man, presented in greater detail in Chapter 6, who came to the psychiatric clinic at his wife's insistence because she was dissatisfied with his effeminacy, in particular his overly "soft" voice. He has been a mama's boy, actually was raised as a girl, and suffers from a lack of aggression and ambition. He relates during interviews in a passively demanding way, wanting to be told what is wrong with him and cooperating with the therapist only so long as he feels something is actively being done to him.

Response to Sound #3: "Sounds like a baby crying out by a pond where there's a bunch of birds. Mother took her baby out by a pond, and there's a lot of birds around making a lot of noise. Just a daily stroll."

Response to Sound #14: "Sounded like a mother that's just finished feeding her child, and she was rocking it and humming a soft lullaby trying to get it to sleep without much success."

Interpretation: Both responses include mother as a guiding and controlling influence. The first one also suggests infantile urinary problems (pond is mentioned twice). The second hints at the mother's failure to soothe and comfort her child (without much success). One really should hear the flat voice accompanying these verbal statements to more fully appreciate this patient's passive-dependency problems.

Patient 5.

This is a 76-year-old man, standoffish, lonely, debilitated, and feeble. While there are no gross physical or mental problems other than those associated with aging, and his hearing is good, admission to the hospital has become necessary because he can no longer sufficiently control his elimination to remain in a residential hotel. He has a slight facial droop and may have had a mild stroke.

Response to Sound #3: "unhuh, uhrrrrruhurrr." (What did you think of that sound?) "Not much." (Recognize it?) "No, sounds like some kids were yelling or something." (?) "I'd say they were young." (?), "a little past the baby stage, four or five." (How many?) "Half a dozen maybe."

Response to Sound #14: "Ah, seems very unhappy. Quarrelling with its parents or something like that."

Interpretation: This man is disgruntled and close to the end of his life. Yet he recognizes youth (kids, young) and multiplies the number of babies he hears in Sound #3 (four or five, half a dozen). Tenderness implied by the lullaby in Sound #14 is reversed, and the patient perceives unhappiness—probably his own —and quarrelling.

These and other results (not presented here) with the Wilmer Test show that acoustic stimulation with pre-recorded sounds can elicit strong emotional reactions. Several listeners imitated the sounds they heard or made various nonlinguistic noises. Most of them spoke about tenderness, urgent calls for help, and other themes appropriately brought into awareness by the sounds of babies. Others denied such themes but did this so forcefully that one may assume that the meanings of baby cries had been correctly recognized.

Since the Wilmer Test actually contains recorded baby sounds it is not surprising that listeners should be able to recognize these sounds. What is truly amazing is the extent to which this severely disturbed group of patients—having organic as well as psychologic difficulties—could recognize these sounds and bring up appropriate emotional and verbal reactions to the stimuli. Some of the patients were quite elderly and hard-of-hearing. Nevertheless their perceptions of baby cries were correct.

THE MASKED BABY CRY

To further study the effects of acoustic stimulation with sounds resembling those described in Chapters 7 and 8, is was necessary to destroy the normal musical pattern of the baby cry and turn it into a kind of noise. This can be accomplished by disguising the baby sounds with a masking noise. A newborn baby was tape-recorded in the nursery, and white noise, generated by means of a Grason Stadler Noise Generator, Model 901A, was added to the tape. The noise was added in such a way that *at the peak of the cries* the total acoustic intensity available from the tape was increased by nine decibels. Most listeners do not show auditory threshold shifts of more than four or five decibels during several minutes of listening (10). Therefore, one can think of these baby cries masked with noise as being subthreshold stimuli, in the sense of subliminal stimulation as used for visual experiments (104).

The acoustic stimulus—baby cries masked nine decibels by noise—was presented through earphones (Clever-Brush) to individual listeners for sixty seconds duration. Each listener was asked to describe the sound he heard, plus any associations, and to return the next day in order to report intercurrent dreams and any subsequent associations to the listening experience. Results are summarized below, with statements that seem to refer to "subliminal" perception of the masked baby cry in italics.

Listener 1: A 28 Year Old Psychiatric Resident

He described the masking noise in the acoustic stimulus as "a loud noise, something like a jet airplane, or an air-blast coming out of a nozzle" and he perceived the hidden baby cry as *"a voice shouting, a man's voice trying to be heard, an agitated sound."* In a dream which had incorporated these percepts, he observed an airplane crash through a window. The scene was visually extremely clear, and he was able to make a drawing of it. Auditorily, it featured the sound of the plane, the crash, and people yelling for help. Among his associations, the most important seemed to be that his wife who was pregnant had recently taken a plane trip to be with her family in a distant city.

Listener 2: A 42 Year Old Record-room Clerk

She described the masking noise as the sound of a "streetcar or train going through a tunnel." Her husband had been a streetcar conductor twenty-five years before, and the sound made her think about this. In her dream there was a person she hadn't seen for years. Visually the dream was very clear, and she described that the person wore a *blue dress.* In another part of the dream she saw "a couple of great big trucks—I could just see their radiators and the grille." According to her description, these grilles matched exactly the grilles over the ceiling lights in the room where the experiment was conducted. When she listened to an unmasked baby cry, she remembered scenes involving her son, specifically one in which he wore a *blue* suit. This was the only association suggesting that she may have previously perceived the masked acoustic stimulus.

Listener 3: A 27 Year Old Psychiatric Resident

He described the masking noise as "static like on a radio" and he heard the subthreshold stimulus as *"something else superimposed over it, like someone yelling and echoing* in a hollow room, probably a woman." His dream was about two sailboats; on the deck of one was a coil of wire or rope shaped like a tunnel. The scene was visualized with great clarity, and had a peculiarly artificial, quiet quality to it. In his associations these coils were connected with some loops of tape he had seen in the office where the experiments were conducted. After listening to the unmasked baby cry, he began to talk of his younger sister who "used to scream quite a bit" and about his own childhood, especially his interest in making paper sailboats.

Listener 4: A 25 Year Old Psychiatric Resident

He is an amateur painter and made a drawing of what he heard as the masking noise: "a visual image of a waterfall coming down, and a rock (94)." He also mentioned the subthreshold stimulus: "Then I became aware of *some sort of cry*—possibly a bird or hawk, maybe a coyote. The cry sounded as though it were echoing between the rocks." In a dream reported the next day, he was walking down a path between eucalyptus trees. The setting reminded him of a grove where he had attended an outdoor concert with his parents several weeks previously. The dream also featured a corral for horses; this was empty, causing him to feel disappointed. His associations were mostly about "scary experiences," and "eerie sensations," and when he relistened to the tape his further associations were about eucalyptus trees as "being wet—the leaves are fish-like, the whole tree seems to move in waves." And finally he said "the corral is like an empty cradle and I think of my sister when she was a *baby*."

Listener 5: A 37 Year Old Social Worker

She described the masking noise as a "scratching kind of noise, like a radio-station that's missed its tuning," and seemed to acknowledge perception also of the hidden cry when she said disappointedly, "I thought there might be a few moments of *human voice coming through*." She described feelings of annoyance, and continued "It's not the kind of noise that I would go seeking out— if I found myself in a situation listening to it, I would immediately get up and *change it*," a statement that also implies recognition of the masked sound. The next day she looked depressed, unkempt, and wore no makeup. She recalled being disturbed by two dreams in the night, recalled her extreme annoyance at "that horrible scratching noise," but could not remember the content of the dreams. When asked to listen to the tape-recording once more, she described "the sea pounding and *a small wail*," and later revealed that on the day of the experiment she had put her young son alone on a jet plane, and that she had felt extremely guilty for thinking that the plane might crash, resulting in his death.

Listener 6: A 29 Year Old Psychiatric Resident

His first association to the sound of the masking noise was "Niagara Falls" and then he thought of a noisy factory with *somebody hammering* in the background, probably referring in this way to some perception of the masked baby cry. He recalled an uncle whose carpenter shop he had visited in his teens. The next day he reported a dream about *"a baby"* and an argument with his wife.

Listener 7: A 33 Year Old Psychiatrist

He described the masking noise as "noise in a place with tremendous machinery, dynamos," and "over it *people seem to be shouting to each other*," apparently a reference to the subliminal baby cry. He reported a memory from childhood, of being in a subway station. A subsequent dream was also about childhood. In it he saw himself visiting a friend but in reality wanting to be with his mother. Possibly the overt expression of this wish bore some relationship to the unconscious perception of the baby cry sound, which previously had been called shouting. In the dream he *called his mother* over the telephone, and then visualized her face.

Listener 8: A 35 Year Old Secretary

She first described the masking noise, and then stated *"you can also hear something else, fluctuating, maybe speech* or part of the noise. I can't identify it—it *goes up and down*." She reported no dreams.

Listener 9: A 25 Year Old Secretary

Her reaction to the masking noise was "Wow—first you hear the crashing of the ocean—then the sound of an orchestra." Her perception of the masked stimulus is revealed by the next statement: *"there's a high sound, ayee, ayee, like a trumpet. It could be somebody yelling, some bellowing."*

It is very striking that none of the listeners failed to perceive the presence of a second stimulus buried in the masking noise, even though the noise they heard covered the peak of the cry sound by nine decibels. Only one listener, the 42 year old record-room clerk, did not directly refer to the masked cry, although her dream suggests that she may have noticed it. This woman mentioned after the experiment (in which she was paid to participate) that she is partially deaf.

To rule out the possibility that the white masking noise might itself be capable of bringing about some of the listener responses attributed above to the hidden baby cry, a control experiment was conducted. The stimulus used this time consisted of a white-noise alone, followed by white-noise masking a baby cry by seven decibels instead of the nine decibels used previously. The listeners this time were instructed to listen for a second sound amidst the noise, to describe fully what they heard, and to discuss any interpretations or associations referable to this auditory experience. The results are tabulated:

Listener	Age	Noise	Noise-plus-cry	Associations
1. Female	51	"I can't hear anything else; my hearing isn't very good."	"There is something there— high-pitched, rhythmic. I can't identify it."	"Maybe running water."
2. Female	40	"Nothing"	"I hear a dog barking, and static."	"It might be a baby crying, or something like that, wind blowing, not just tone."
3. Male	20	"I just thought that it's time to have lunch."	"I hear something."	"Yea, you can hear a baby crying in the background."
4. Female	23	No reaction—she kept on reading a book by Thomas Wolfe that she had brought to the laboratory.	"I can hear something."	"It was a dog barking like what I'd imagine a bloodhound to sound like; kind of whining or maybe the sound of machinery scraping."
5. Male	35	"Just noise."	"Yea, I hear a dog barking, going ahooa, ahooa, ahooa."	"Yes, I'm sure it sounded like a dog barking."

All of the control listeners were able to differentiate white-noise alone from the masked baby cry stimulus. Some of the qualitative attributes of the cries were even mentioned, such as high-pitch and rhythmicity. The masked cry was also described as barking, whining, or onomatopoeically as "ahooa." White-noise alone never produced such reactions. While the number of subjects is quite small, the control experiment does make it seem unlikely that crying sounds reported by listeners were based on the perception of masking noise per se. Also the more definite responses of control listeners to cries masked seven decibels as compared with the more vague responses of experimental listeners to cries masked nine decibels (the same cries were used for both runs) suggest that while masking did in fact occur, the white-noise did not completely disrupt the acoustic pattern of the baby cry. Enough of the signal evidently came through the earphones to tell the experimental subjects that there was more to this than just noise.

Why some listeners more rapidly and correctly recognized the masked sound cannot be determined without closer study of the individual subjects. Those with prior musical training for instance may have been more responsive to the sound of the hidden cry. Certainly the listener who was deaf in one ear would not be expected to hear cry (or noise) as well as other subjects. But since we have been more concerned so far with characteristics of the acoustic stimulus than with auditory skills or abilities of listeners, another experiment must be conducted, one which studies the value, or meaningfulness, of known acoustic stimuli and tests the preferential responses of unidentified listeners to these known sounds.

CHILDREN'S VOICES

Neither listening situation just described—the Wilmer Test nor the Masked Baby Cry experiment—gave listeners any choice as to what to do. Sounds were simply presented to listeners, whose responses were observed, and who were asked to talk about their thoughts, dreams, and emotional reactions. How difficult it is to describe what one hears has already been emphasized in Chapter 3. Add to this the inconvenience of having to do this at an experimenter's request and only in response to sounds which he preselects and controls, and you have a situation which bears very little similarity to normal life. Conclusions about human listening behavior based on the findings of such experiments must be taken with many grains of salt—yet, for better or for worse, much information about listening found in textbooks is actually obtained in this way (73).

A somewhat more true-to-life experiment allows listeners to exercise some control over stimuli to which they are exposed. Not only their responses but also the pattern of stimulus-selection can then be studied; the latter is particularly relevant to the interesting problem of auditory preference with which we are now concerned. One purpose of the following study was to rate the popularity—in an adult psychiatric ward—of sounds produced by little children. We have already called attention to the loudness of baby sounds, and certain acoustic characteristics like sharpness and high-pitch which seem to make infantile sounds easily heard. Moreover, we know from empirical observation and from the two experiments just reported that baby cries are very powerful stimuli—in both an acoustical and an emotional sense. It is to be expected therefore that cries, cry-like sounds, and other acoustic patterns reminiscent of the helplessness and vulnerability of childhood might be extremely unwelcome in a ward full of emotionally disturbed adults.

To study this matter, a juke-box was installed on the ward. The loudspeaker was placed into the ceiling of the day-room, and a small control-panel was put near the door so that patients in the room could select what sounds to hear. Five classes of sound were tested for popularity by means of fifteen phonograph records (30 selections in all) placed randomly into the juke-box. The classes, records, and frequencies of selection are tabulated in Table VI. For three months, during which there was little turnover of patients and no rotation of doctors, nurses, or other professional personnel on the ward, the record-player was left on the ward, and patients were encouraged to select from the control panel the acoustic environments which they found most pleasing and desirable.

The juke-box was played altogether 1,591 times in the three

TABLE VI

POPULARITY RANKING OF FIVE CLASSES OF SOUNDS IN AN
ADULT PSYCHIATRIC WARD

Rank*	Sound	Class	Number of Times Selected
1	Strauss Waltzes (Boston Pops)	5	275
2	Songs (Julie London)	3	203
3	Blues (Duke Ellington)	5	193
4	Exotica (Martin Denny)	5	184
5	Songs (Eddie Fisher)	1	162
6	Sousa Marches (Boston Pops)	5	116
7	Songs (Jan Peerce)	1	100
8	Songs (Arthur Godfrey)	1	70
9.5	Songs (Dorothy Olsen)	3	57
9.5	Noises (Wild animals, cathedral bells)	4	57
11.5	Narration (Billy Vaughn)	1	52
11.5	Noises (Heartbeats, respiration, birds)	4	52
13	Noises (Surf, sucking)	4	32
14	Songs (Cricketone chorus)	2	23
15	Songs (Robin Morgan)	2	8
		Total	1591

Classes: 1—Male Voice
2—Children's Voices
3—Female Voice
4—Noises
5—Instrumental Music

---

* This rank order has been compared with a random frequency distribution, and the probability of getting the distribution shown on the Table is less than 2 per cent.

month interval. Table VI shows the pattern of selection: a record of Strauss waltzes was played 275 times in three months, achieving the highest popularity rating; a record of children's songs by Robin Morgan was played only eight times. This and another record of children's sounds—Mother Goose songs rendered by a group of infantile baby voices—was the most unpopular selection from the juke-box ($p \leq .02$). It is interesting to see also that nonvocal and nonmusical noises (physiological sounds, surf-sounds, bells, and animal screeches) were not very popular among the patients. One of the best-liked records was that of lullabies sung in a maternal and tranquilizing way by Julie London.

SUMMARY

We return in this chapter to the crying behavior of babies,

but now study—instead of soundmakers—the reactions of listeners to such sounds. Two acoustic stimuli from an auditory projective test devised by Wilmer feature baby cries, and these were used to elicit verbal responses from five patients. While in general the patients reacted to the recorded cries in a strongly emotional way, more would have to be known about the psychopathology and life histories of these individuals to explain their behavior. An experiment with baby cries whose peaks have been masked by the addition of nine decibels of white noise is next presented. The results, while tentative, indicate that the cry remained recognizable and capable of eliciting specific reactions from listeners even in the face of such an acoustically distorting procedure. Finally, a popularity poll was conducted among listeners on a hospital ward by means of a juke box, which automatically tabulated the sounds they chose to listen to. Of 1591 choices made over a three-month period, selections which featured children's voices were played only 31 times, indicating a significant trend against these sounds. While such a trend cannot be explained without further investigation, it should encourage us to pay close attention to the auditory needs and preferences of emotionally disturbed patients, and alert us to the potential value of therapeutically structuring the acoustic environments of psychiatric hospitals.

Chapter 10

NONSPEAKING PATIENTS

To view soundmaking as an exchange of acoustic signals, and then to study the production and the reception of sounds exchanged, constitutes a laudable scientific pursuit and poses innumerable technical challenges. Yet clinicians see acoustic communication in terms that are even more complex than what has been hinted at in preceding chapters: Two entire personality organizations are involved—that of the soundmaker and that of the listener—plus the innumerable physical and social conditions of their environment. Fine-grained acoustical study of sounds should reveal much fascinating detail, but it always threatens to blur what in many respects is a more important part of communication—the human problem. Disturbed soundmakers (patients) in particular are entitled first of all to humane consideration by virtue of being sick persons. Treating them as laboratory specimens may do an injustice to patients, and also may fool the experimenter because it deprives him of significant data about personal aspects of their soundmaking.

This and the following chapter sheds the meticulosity of the laboratory in order to recreate something of the drama of actual disturbed soundmaking as witnessed in a mental hospital. Four patients will be discussed: each represents an example of one of psychiatry's greatest riddles—the person who makes grossly aberrant sounds in spite of the fact that his physical apparatus for acoustic communication is not demonstrably impaired. There are many different diagnostic labels for these nonspeaking patients—autism, schizophrenia, mental retardation, hebephrenia, and others. Since we shall focus here on disturbances in soundmaking, these diagnostic terms and the psychopathologic distinctions therein contained will not be of primary concern.

AN AUTISTIC CHILD

Bob is eight years old and a bright, cheerful-looking youngster. But his gestures and speech pattern make it clear that he is not a normal boy. Generally rather overactive, restless, and unmanageable, he suddenly darts about the room or stays too long in a single immobile posture. After some acquaintance with him, one becomes aware of a certain grimace-like quality to his facial expressions. Also, the boy sometimes moves his hands in a strange but repetitive way, suggesting that he is engaged in doing something meaningful, but that he cannot get others to share this meaning by communicating in a code they understand. For example, he moves his flat palm back and forth from his knees to his genital region, or from one knee up to his face.

From a soundmaking point of view, the most remarkable thing about Bob is his very personal use of spoken language. When he speaks it is not with the sentence or word patterns one customarily hears in conversation. He does not ask questions, give replies, render descriptions, or make complaints. Instead, emission of speech sounds appears to be mainly a self-directed activity. Bob's soundmaking seems to be a kind of acoustic game, much like the babbling of babies which has little to do with the sort of communication aiming for outsider participation. Particularly with proper nouns, like the names of other persons, Bob does something very peculiar for a boy his age: he repeats, rhymes, and endlessly shuffles and reshuffles the component sounds (the phonemes and morphemes) of the words. In effect, in this boy's mouth, names lose all significance as labels for things and people.

Bob also tampers with other parts of speech. By incessantly distorting the rhythmicity, intensity, pitch, tone, speed, shape, and orderliness pattern of spoken language he makes it impossible for any listener to put the linguistic cues—phonemes, morphemes, and words—into any properly meaningful relationships. He seems to lack the capacity for adhering to those linguistic constraints which control verbal soundmaking, but instead produces sounds because they rhyme, resemble each other onomatopoeically, or are simply fun to mouth.

One might suppose that Bob's peculiar ways with speech represent his ignorance of the formal rules of spoken discourse. That such is not the case becomes evident if one engages the boy in one of his favorite games, "alphabet." He knows all the letters of the alphabet and can hook them up to words. While this is sometimes done on the basis of acoustic similarity, for instance "J is for Georgia," he usually correctly (and somewhat precociously) spells out various words, even difficult ones. More evidence that he formally understands language is obtained if one asks him to do things; without replying he will promptly and correctly obey your verbal command. Tell him to pick up an envelope lying on a nearby table and put it in your hand, and he does so. Ask him whether what you hold in your hand is a key and he correctly replies with a nod—but without a sound. Obviously he understands—but cannot use—linguistic forms.

Bob seems incredibly sensitive to nuances—for instance of pitch— in the pronunciation of words. He often mimics what he hears, disregarding entirely the meaning of the words, which are employed rather as vehicles for his soundmaking. This misuse of language appears to amuse him, and he takes even more delight in soundplay when it obviously confounds other listeners. He also likes to entertain others by repeating various catchy slogans, jingles, and alliterative phrases which he has heard on radio or television commercials. Even the way Bob mispronounces these slogans indicates his utter disregard for the precision of speech: he leaves out significant sounds and scrambles some of the others. For example, "I use superblue blade" (sic) is one of his favorite phrases, but he does not bother to give the blades the necessary pluralizing /s/. Similarly, "I use pumolive rapinshave" is uttered without proper linguistic regard either for the manufacturer or the shaving cream. This preoccupation with shaving topics also says something about problems of sexual identification and castration anxiety which underlie the emotional illness of which this boy's soundmaking pathology is but one symptom.

Sometimes Bob's soundmaking becomes a pseudolanguage. He strings a sequence of phonemes together in such a way that this resembles the sound of words but never actually comes close enough to known words to make sense, analogous to the way that Danny Kaye mimics foreigners without actually using words of the foreign language. Bob seems to be unaware of the annoying effect that this has on others. His use of pseudolanguage creates an ambivalent, double-bind situation for any listener, since simultaneously he "makes words" that invite your attention and then disappoints you with meaningless utterances. This puts the listener into the uncomfortable situation of having at the same time to open and to close his ears, a situation which may lead to intolerable conflict and tension if one is habitually exposed to it (8).

There are also times however that Bob seems deeply distressed by stalemates which result from his very peculiar ways of making sound. He then repeats with increasing vigor one particular kind of acoustic pattern, a stereotyped form of soundmaking which seems to imply "I want something." This repetitive, demanding, insistent manner of soundmaking may involve one of his typical phoneme-salads, for instance /aiskob-aiskob-aiskob/. He also may use stereotyped pitch patterns to drive his wishes home. For example, Bob often uses an upward pitch glide followed by a downward pitch glide. This particular inflection sequence is very reminiscent of the baby cry sound (see Chapter 4) and often has the expected result on listeners; the cry-like pitch pattern effectively cuts through his spoken words much like the tape-recorded baby cry discussed in Chapter 9 which was audible in spite of an intense masking noise. For example, in one interview he uttered "I've got a pump" with the last word lengthily drawn out and intoned with a whining, downward wail. His therapist did not immediately respond to this, and the patient followed it up with "I want to go home," uttered with the identical pitch inflection pattern as the previous phrase. After several further such acoustic outbursts, the therapist began to realize that Bob was expressing his desire to be relieved of some sort of intense internally-felt pressure, the word "pump" suggesting that perhaps bladder urgency was involved.

Half-octave band measurement of Bob's speech before and during one of these cry-like outbursts is shown in the top half of Figure 18. A dashed curve denotes the linguistically comprehensible utterance "where is my doctor," uttered in a blunt, aggressive-sounding flat voice. Acoustically, this sound shows motant 1 rather broad and centered at 250 cps; motant 2 is flat-topped in the center of the acoustic spectrum; motant 3 comes to a peak at 2,000 cps. Compare this with the solid curve which denotes a ro-

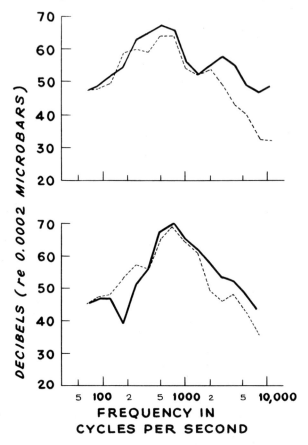

Fig. 18. Half-octave band measurements of two types of sound produced by an autistic child. The upper graph displays two verbal fragments, one more loud and robust (solid curve) due to its enhancement by a paralinguistic cry (see text for details). The lower graph displays a bit of pseudo-language, the word /aiskob/ emitted much like the cry of a baby (compare this graph with Fig. 7, Chapter 4).

bust cry-like outburst "I use a razor" that comes to a climax on the first syllable of "razor": Motants 1 and 2 are fused into one large area of acoustic energy concentration centered at 500 cps which reaches a level of 67 decibels. There is a second very prominent area of energy concentration centered at 2,860 cps. The cry-like sound (8.3 sones) is 25 percent louder than the more normal sound (6.2 sones).

Half-octave band measurement of some of Bob's nonsense jargoniz-ing (bottom half of Fig. 18) shows even more clearly the re-semblance between this patient's soundmaking and the cry-sound of young babies. The fragment denoted here is the sound /aiskob/. The first part, /ais/, is emitted in a scream-like manner that shows no clear differentiation of motants but simply a sharp peaking of acoustic energy at 715 cps (solid curve). The second part, /kob/, has more the acoustic characteristics of speech in that the funda-mental tone is defined as motant 1 at 250 cps, while resonance energy is found in motant 2 centered at 715 cps (dashed curve).

A SCHIZOPHRENIC ADOLESCENT

Mary is fourteen years old and was admitted to a mental hospital at age six. She is a terrible behavior problem, soils, wets, and masturbates herself openly. She smears food and feces on her clothes and body, and alternates between eroticism, withdrawal, and assaultiveness in her behavior towards staff members and other patients. Mary's mother believes that the trouble began when the girl was only two weeks old and "turned away from my breast." To what extent this mother's inability to be normally affectionate towards her daughter has been a re-sponsible factor in the child's abnormal development cannot be determined with certainty. The fact is that the mother became pregnant when Mary was two months old and at that time lost interest in her. Also, it is interesting that Mary's admission to the hospital coincided with the birth of a second sister. Mary's mother cannot definitely pinpoint any psychopathology before the age of two years, which was when she noted that the girl "acted deaf," ignored questions and remarks from others, but while alone would talk and sing to herself normally. Throughout the next year, Mary learned new words and phrases, but used these only to talk to herself and never for communication with others.

Little speech development has been noticed during the eight years since Mary entered the hospital. She seldom uses words, but emits instead numerous crude body sounds like burps, slurps, sneezes, and snorts. This occurs most noticeably whenever she engages in animal-like explorations of the environment; she sniffs the air, smells and licks various objects, drools and slobbers over herself and on others. Only when she becomes pleasurably absorbed in some activity—drawing, clay-modelling, or doll play—does Mary emit any sounds resembling words. She ejects these sounds rather explosively, like bullets from a machine-gun, in simple one- or two-syllable fragments. The sounds are invariably screechy, raspy, and ugly in quality, more reminiscent of animal noises than human speech. Intonation patterns are quite stereotyped, and often fall into mechanical-sounding sing-song patterns that span a tone range of as much as one octave.

During a playroom session that was tape-recorded, Mary emitted a total of 323 such sounds. Her therapist stimulated this soundmaking by repeating each sound after her as soon as it was uttered, nodding his head, and generally indicating approval of her behavior. A transcript of the sounds appears on Table VII. Forty-two per cent of the sounds seem to resemble words referring to foods (e.g., cheese, cookie, milk); 26 per cent of the sounds are noises or nonsense sounds (e.g., glofoo, buud, ssu), and less than 1 per cent (only two words) of the sounds refer to people. (The remaining 31 per cent refer mainly to items of clothing, furniture, and a few descriptive adjectives.) In addition to the high proportion of food words among her sounds, there appears to be an overlap between certain food words and the onomatopoeic noises she produces. Take this sequence of sounds for example: (noise), ch hee hoo, hemo, hemo, hemo, eee-o, hee mos, cupcakes." She starts with a noise and gradually comes closer to a food word (hemo), perseverates on this, goes back to an onomatopoeia ("eee-o" for hemo), and then switches to "cupcakes."

TABLE VII

CONSECUTIVE SOUNDS MADE BY A SCHIZOPHRENIC GIRL IN THE PLAYROOM

	Categories	Number	Per Cent
1	objects	74	23
2	food	136	42
3	abstract forms	26	8
4	noise and nonsense	85	26
5	people	2	1
	Total	323	100

Sound	Category	Sound	Category
(noise)	4	hemo	2
brellow	4	hemo	2
(noise)	4	hemo	2
hhh	4	eee - O	4
sheets	1	he mos	2
pen	1	cupcakes	2
macaroni	2	anayaya	4
cheese	2	mmm	4
treats	2	buud	4
freezer	1	(noise)	4
nh crackers	2	grruh peow	4
sleepy sheets	1	hynmmee	4
n - sheets	1	hotcakes	2
fricky sheets	1	helayee	4
aahaah	4	what the	3
whee	4	sss	4
bub	4	tu tuhh	4
is the ham cooked	2	cookies	2
(noise)	4	hotcakes	2
ammm	4	n - syrup	2
aahah	4	yellow	3
mm uh mm uh	4	uh	4
(noise)	4	chocolate bunny	2
sugar sh sugar	2	ice cream	2
butter	2	hotcakes	2
mmm	4	hemo	2
cow's milk	2	dress sss	1
(noise)	4	pants	1
cow's milk	2	shoes	1
sugar	2	socks	1
put some cheeze in it	2	comb and a brush	1
(noise)	4	m butter	2
m butter	2	cow	1
cheeze	2	(noise)	4
sugar	2	shsh	4
(noise)	4	s socks	1
banana	2	escopibble	4
mm	4	oh	4
n - sugar	2	water	2
apple ceekies	2	feet	1
(noise)	4	woola	4
ee o	4	fa	4
dld	4	shirt	1
(noise)	4	puddy	4
lullie	4	pillowcase	1
pineapple cookies	2	shirt	1
(noise)	4	clean	3
ch hee hoo	4	clean	3

Sound	Category	Sound	Category
box	1	cookie	2
ala safetypin	1	bag	1
pillowdo case	1	barrels	1
shirts	1	doors	1
shoes	1	yellow	3
box	1	talk pretty	3
bag	1	are you sleepy	3
tweets	4	but the biscuit cue	2
biscuits	2	strawberries	2
ice cream	2	orange juice	2
pen	1	cinnamon	2
spoon	1	biscuit	2
egg	2	treats	2
fweezer	1	eggs	2
bre-	4	ah sugar	2
sugar	2	bag	1
mm bandaids	1	cheese	2
dwars	4	turkey	2
stwawberries	2	spoonspoons	1
box	1	bag	1
wish	3	spoons	1
wish	3	egg	2
box	1	meatloaf	2
doors	1	bud	4
costs	1	dadadee	4
glofoo	4	cookies	2
box	1	candies	2
(noise)	4	coacoa	2
hmm	4	coca cola	2
go to bed	3	n - cheese	2
goodnight	3	m m m mush	2
ch - whoy fish	2	sugar	2
ow	4	ma -	4
socks	1	pan	1
whatsamatter	3	mush	2
what	3	fweezer	1
beebee	4	cows milk	2
ow	4	spoons	1
fleebess	4	cream	2
(noise)	4	cream	2
biscuit	2	mush	2
cowsmilk	2	butter	2
eggs	2	cheeze	2
cheese	2	butter	2
spoon	1	butter	2
cheese	2	(noise)	4
buiscuit	2	hotcake	2
cows milk	2	eggs	2

Sound	Category	Sound	Category
yellow	3	mat	1
cookie	2	poopoo	4
butter	2	flowers	1
sugar	2	sugar	2
take your bath	3	mush	2
peepytail	4	milk	2
whoorat	4	feezer	1
(noise)	4	m matress	1
m butter	2	drawers	1
eggs 'n milk	2	glass	1
(noise)	4	candy	2
crackers	2	cheese	2
butter	2	milk	2
peepytail	4	hot	3
mbath tub	1	nourishment	2
cookie (whisper)	2	want gulp	2
easter	3	records	1
mat	1	cowboy	1
house	1	ta tatata	4
whahappened	3	easter	3
mmbum	4	l - ice cream	2
mush	2	ice cream cups	2
scrabble	1	banana bowl	2
scrabble	1	cookie	2
(noise)	4	doughnut	2
butterer	2	na buiscuit	2
st-stink	3	marshmallow	2
st-ppuddy	4	nut	2
cute	3	banana	2
sleepy	3	coke	2
mbuiscuits	2	m raisins	2
feeda	4	candy	2
cowsmilk	2	biscuits	2
water alone	2	cocoas	2
matress	1	yum	4
drawers	1	milk	2
biscuit	2	mjam	2
treat	2	ha h ch m	4
banana bowl	2	m apple sauce	2
milk	2	spoons	1
cocoa	2	cantalope	2
spoons	1	packatapata	4
gingerale	2	m balls	1
banana	2	whazzamatter	3
ice cream	2	ah	4
strawberries	2	(noise)	4
buiscuits	2	ch shirt	1
treat	2	puddy	4

Sound	Category	Sound	Category
pretty shirt	1	(noise)	4
pillow case	1	m - cheese	2
clean	3	sugar	2
ironing	3	sugar	2
shirts	1	(noise)	4
pillow cases	1	mm - n	4
bas	4	ssu	4
safety pin	1	cole	3
mn Suzie	5	ch	4
sh carolyne	5	pigs	1
slamy	2	k	4
ham	2	d - pillowcase	1
n rice	2	shirts	1
spaghetti	2	pam pam pam	4
cheese	2	preddy shirts	1
m flashbu	4	(noise)	4
gallica	4	butter butter	2

Table VII denotes Mary's sounds nonphonetically as words. Actually this does the patient's soundmaking an injustice, since her utterances are not standard English in any real sense, but more a kind of sloppy mimicry of English speech. For instance, she says "puddy" for pretty, and "dwars" for drawers. Also she fails to make the necessary pauses and junctures between words, as for instance when she says "whazzamatter." Furthermore, her productions are replete with neologistic word combinations based on rhyming or repetition of sounds: e.g., "spoonspoons," "pillowdo case." When she emits complete phrases such as "are you sleepy" or "take your bath," these sound as though they have been directly lifted out of context from someone else's speech and are being mimicked without regard to the meaning of the words.

How does Mary function in settings outside the playroom? One big event in her life at the hospital is to be allowed to use the ward kitchen and prepare herself a steak dinner. A nurse assists her in this task, brings the necessary ingredients and utensils into the room, and tries to prevent Mary from spilling things or burning herself on the hot stove. The entire kitchen experience is an adventure in nonsymbolic communication for our patient. Not once does she talk about what she does; she never asks for advice or questions the presence of onlookers.

Hungrily she smells the meat, potatoes, and vegetables of her meal, like a little puppy. She apparently relishes every moment of the culinary act, even the hissing of the frying steak, for she gleefully imitates this by making little hissing noises with her mouth. From time to time she will similarly imitate a sound of the nurse who, in spite of the primarily nonverbal transactions going on between herself and the patient, occasionally must render some verbal instructions such as "watch out, the pan's hot." In mimicking the nurse, the patient almost mouths her words as though these were as tangible and edible a part of the environment as the steak in her frying pan. This echolalia seems part of the patient's attempt to relate directly to her environment, her seeking immediate and real contact without having to cope with the ambiguities of word symbols (135).

A MENTALLY RETARDED YOUTH (AND HIS MOTHER)

At the age of twenty-one, Patrick was brought to the clinic for "speech training." Since his mother accompanied him and did all the talking, let us meet her first:

Over the telephone, Patrick's mother sounds like a sad and rather helpless person. Her voice is monotonous and a bit on the querulous side. But when she comes to the clinic and one encounters her visually, the impression she creates is quite different: she is a big, square, hefty woman. Her face, while not unattractive, looks masculine, and her silver-gray hair is cut short and lies close and neat against her head. She wears simple clothes, black dress, and a gray coat, but obtrusive cheap jewelry which gives her a kind of hard, insincere elegance. Very striking is that she never closes her mouth while speaking; the lips are set firmly, but usually parted; the upper lip is often drawn up in what appears like a sneer. She talks rapidly and circumstantially, in the sad tone of voice so obvious over the telephone. There is a trace of foreign dialect, and occasionally poor grammar breaks through, but it would be difficult to recognize her true background from speech and appearance. Only the hands, arms, and legs are clearly those of a working person—heavy, mannish, and coarse, without grooming.

Patrick's mother was born in Ireland, of parents who were

devout Catholics and worked on a farm. The children came to the United States to be employed as domestics in wealthy families. Patrick's mother always had been fond of caring for children and at about age twenty, she started work as a governess, taking care of a little girl. At age twenty-six, she met and married a man whose childhood had been spent in an orphanage.

Patrick was their first child. While awaiting his birth in the hospital, his mother met a young French girl who was also in labor. The baby, named Patricia, arrived several hours before Patrick, and the two new mothers compared the progress of their children very closely during the first few years. "Patricia had a head-start, but soon was overtaken by my boy. He was breastfed until five and one-half months of age and fully weaned by seven and one-half months. He hummed songs before the age of one year." According to his mother, Patrick, like all her children, was "broken" before the age of one year; bowel training began at seven months, and by the age of eleven months "he was able to go to the potty unassisted." Bladder training was completed shortly thereafter. In other respects the boy was also quite advanced. Before the age of one, he could feed himself, put his shoes on, and say simple sentences like: "Daddy go work," "go bye bye," "trowdada," and "dear I come (sic)."

The mother dates the onset of Patrick's psychopathology to the age of fifteen months when, during a visit with Patricia there was a fight over toys. "She screamed at him and he got scared and very nervous." His previously rapid speech development declined, and he began to use actions instead of words to express himself. At age two years, he regressed to bedwetting for about six months. About this time, he also began to request "two" of everything, such as cookies or toys. Patrick always liked to be held, but when he found out his mother was pregnant, he gradually gave this up. He would stroke his mother's bulging abdomen and say "lovely baby," and when his brother was born he became protective towards the baby. His mother says, "Patrick has always been very sensitive to other people's feelings."

Since this time, age two and one-half, Patrick has been more or less of an invalid at home. According to his mother, pediatricians advised her that "he should be given time to grow up." But at age five, Patrick was so "nervous" that no nursery school would take him. His mother disregarded the doctor's advice for a hands-off policy and made arrangements for special education "because he was retarded." His adjustment was very poor, and at eight he started to have noisy temper tantrums.

For years since then, Patrick has been taken to many different clinics; in pediatric and speech clinics he is labeled mentally retarded, and in psychiatric clinics he is called schizophrenic. To date no treatment or education measures have appreciably altered his behavior. For a while his parents visited a mental hygiene clinic in order to help Patrick by modifying their overprotective attitudes, but even this failed to enable the boy to develop any useful degree of speech or to manage a life away from his family. Nevertheless his mother continues to have hope; she awaits "a miracle from God to cure Patrick." She is pleased that "fortunately Patrick has no sex problems," and she proclaims her willingness to take care of him until she dies. Patrick is a good helper at home and assists his mother with household chores. The mother's main objection is that his peculiar behavior and inability to talk attracts attention. She wants him to have speech lessons "so he can learn to say what he wants."

Patrick is thin and tall, with a gaunt, aquiline face. He rarely looks at anyone. He makes many audible sounds both spontaneously and in reply to questions, but seldom do these form words. Occasionally, a string of his noises resembles the sound of a newsreport on the radio, due to similarity in rhythmicity of these sound patterns. But there are actually no sentences, and nothing Patrick emits makes any denotative sense. Sometimes he breathes heavily, and if one listens closely, this turns out to be a blurred and low-intensity form of speech mimicry. Patrick mumbles silently to himself throughout inspiration as well as expiration, but this raspy noise too is unintelligible. Even when Patrick makes a real effort to talk his sounds still are very difficult to recognize as words. One reason for this is that he seldom closes his mouth and almost never elevates his velum to keep from nasalizing. Consequently air rushes out through his flaccidly parted lips and the unobstructed nasal passageway, giving all vocal sounds a hollow, mushy, grunting quality (33). He also emits audible noises by rectum quite frequently; in fact flatulence constitutes for Patrick an important means for communication, since people then notice his stink as well as his noise. Particularly when angry, or when his formless oral expulsion of air seems not to get through to people, the patient produces an audible and smellable anal message.

A HEBEPHRENIC MAN

The most unintelligible man in a large State Hospital is Mr. Cooper, age forty-two. He was admitted following a brief schizophrenic excitement during his seventeenth year. To get to the hospital required a long train trip, and the railway conductor became something of a beacon for the patient in his distress. He also clung fearfully to a policeman who in the absence of his parents accompanied him during the journey. Consequently for some years thereafter whenever Mr. Cooper was asked who he is, he replied "I am a railway conductor" or "I am a policeman," depending on which one of the two authority figures who had strongly impressed him dominated his thoughts. After twenty-five years of custodial care plus occasional electroconvulsive treatments, he presents the following clinical picture.

Short and rather squat in shape, Mr. Cooper holds his heavy arms close to his body and peers out through myopic, intelligent-looking eyes. In a different setting, he might be mistaken for an intellectual, scholar, or scientist. He shakes hands in a friendly way, but these feel like inert lumps of refrigerated meat. Mr. Cooper doesn't talk. He communicates entirely by means of gestures, plus an unarticulated vocal stream of sounds. His lips don't close and none of the muscles around his mouth ever really move. Consequently communication is impeded on two scores: 1) the lack of mouth articulation drastically reduces intelligibility of any sounds he makes, and 2) his mask-like, stiff-upper-lip face prevents onlookers from visually recognizing what he may be feeling (105).

In other respects Mr. Cooper relates to his environment either very intently or not at all. When he is "with you," he gesticulates and vigorously grunts, resembling a person who does not speak your language, yet tries to make himself understood. Occasionally he even performs a little pantomime: for example, by crossing his forearms and placing the hands on his shoulders, he mimics a straight-jacketed prisoner; by tapping his temples and uttering bizarre, unintelligible sounds, he portrays a blatantly insane man. When he is withdrawn from the environment, he sits or stands with shoulders stooped and head bent forward, mumbling to himself while harshly breathing in and out. Suddenly, he will glance upward and look alertly at you, which makes one suspect that his stupor is partly feigned and that he still has the ability to make contact with his environment at times.

Since none of Mr. Cooper's sounds are words, one must help him find other symbolic ways to communicate. Offered pencil and paper, he eagerly seizes these and starts to draw. Invariably the drawings are the same: a pattern of horizontal and vertical lines that intersect to produce squares, upon which some diagonal lines forming crosses are superimposed. These drawings are carefully executed without haste or disorder. Each one has a margin border on the right, and the horizontal lines are meticulously prevented from running into this. Only once, when specifically asked to draw circles, does he add something else to a drawing: a series of oval concentric circles. When he is finished he responds to questions about his productions by vigorously pointing to the center of each drawing and uttering an unintelligible sound [zə́hɔ] which seems to be a vaguely echolalic response to the question, "Is that something?"

Could Mr. Cooper's little drawings represent a barred window or cell behind which a person is imprisoned? When confronted with this interpretation he looks dumbfounded; he neither agrees nor disagrees; he cannot seem to cope with the verbal formulation. Therefore, we will never know whether this interpretation of his marks on paper corresponds with anything that he may have in mind. When asked about the circles he has drawn, the patient again utters an inarticulate sound, one which resembles the word "mother." But as before, a verbal exchange about this is impossible, and he neither confirms nor denies this interpretation of his soundmaking. Asked once more whether he said "mother," he becomes excited, grunts, and gesticulates even more wildly; but this excitement does not tell us whether the interpretation is wrong, nor does it dissuade one from feeling that perhaps it is correct after all. Such a "conversation" with Mr. Cooper is reminiscent of what happens when one tries to discuss the "meaning" of an abstract painting, poem, or work of music. Since the symbols are nonrepresentational, it is impossible ever to agree or disagree about any denotative meanings imposed on them.

Mr. Cooper's handicap in denotative communication becomes further apparent when one asks him to write his name. He puts down only the first name, in a childish scrawl, and makes a mistake in spelling, leaving out important letters. Ask him to count, and he correctly writes down the numbers one through six; then he stops. Told to write the number seven, he complies with great effort, and finally writes this figure in reverse. What is the significance of this cipher, and why is it reversed? Perhaps this has something to do with age seventeen, when he became disturbed and was put in the hospital. Again, to question him about this is useless; our questions and his responses to them seem to be in two different languages. One feels like a foreigner trying to communicate with a native in the absence of an interpreter. If we refer to the theme of age and years nonverbally by whistling "Happy Birthday to You," this only confounds the patient, who then stops gesticulating and soundmaking, and withdraws into a kind of reverie state.

SUMMARY

Communication disturbances of four nonspeaking patients are presented in this chapter. The first patient is a young boy who produced jargon, gibberish, and cry-like utterances. The second is an adolescent girl who made chains of semi-intelligible noises referring mainly to food. The third patient has been autistic since early childhood; he made crude oral grunts and anal noises. The last patient has lived for years in a state hospital; he communicated with enigmatic grimaces, sounds and gestures. Phenomenologically these patients seem in certain respects different from clinical syndromes like schizophrenia and mental retardation with which they are often classified. I have therefore tried to describe their soundmaking pathology in detail, to see what underlying factors these cases may have in common. None of the patients seemed able to grasp the logic of verbal discourse. Their sound-making, while in certain superficial ways resembling speech, appeared primarily playful and could not be used for the exchange of abstract thoughts. This kind of problem puts the psychiatrist at a disadvantage; unable to speak together, doctor and patient can seldom substantiate any hypotheses about psychogenic and psychodynamic elements of the disease. To do this, one would first have to make contact with the patient at the level of play and nonverbal interaction. Later a detailed analysis of the sounds might enable the therapist—through mimicry and onomatopoeia—to provide sufficient external feedback to get a relationship going in which denotative speech could ultimately be used.

Chapter 11

DISTURBED SOUNDMAKERS

The patients presented in Chapter 10 are all extremely unsocial and can live only under the most limited circumstances of freedom. They must be constantly watched over and given assistance by members of their families or by the staff of a mental hospital. The soundmaking of these patients is characterized by a tendency to emit garbled phonetic material, pseudolanguage, primitive cry-like noises, or to remain silent. Often their mouths do not close; when they do speak, the sound comes out as through a megaphone which can only amplify but not modulate. Attempts to interact with these patients by way of verbal discourse are frustrating and often hopeless.

There are also some very disturbed soundmakers who live and work in the community-at-large. Often these patients are quite successful in some walk of life—say in business or as students—and this helps keep their abnormal soundmaking from becoming too noticeable or too disturbing to others. Usually these patients can speak; they can think, say, and use words at certain times in such ways as to be practically indistinguishable from normal speech. But there is a difference which becomes apparent —as we shall see—when the patient is under stress or has to speak about embarrassing personal problems.

The difference between normal and disturbed speech often lies less in the acoustic product than in the psychology of the soundmaker: unlike normal speakers, many disturbed soundmakers are unable to emit sounds without thinking or feeling that this behavior also has some purpose other than symbolic communication. These are often lonely, unhappy, secretly frustrated persons who unconsciously yearn for a direct physical contact with listeners instead of the indirect symbolic contact provided by speech. Activation of the soundmaking organs may remind such persons that these parts of the body must also be available for biological acts that do not lead to speech. Thus for them speaking is too readily associated with sucking, chewing, biting, licking, spitting, swallowing, breathing, laughing, crying, coughing, sneezing, vomiting, and other nonlinguistic forms of soundmaking.

Whereas normal speakers successfully cope with this multiplicity of functions inherent in the soundmaking organs, the disturbed person cannot so readily direct the activity of these organs solely toward speech (48). He may be burdened by unconscious associations between sounds and nonacoustic products of the soundmaking organs like spit, vomit, or hot air. It may even happen—as in the case of Patrick in Chapter 10—that disturbed soundmakers feel compelled to engage the rectum for soundmaking (81). Other patients may have similar fixations in body areas that only indirectly give off noise—e.g., the urethra and the sounds of urination (38). Here are some examples of disturbed soundmakers.

A MALE NURSE WHO STUTTERS

At the age of twenty-two this patient is not certain whether he is to be a man or a woman. He is ambitious, has a steady job, looks and dresses well, and is outwardly aggressive and sociable. But his love relationships and sexual activities involve men only. While he may date girls, flirt with them and go to dances, his enjoyment of these pursuits is really based on a feeling of mutuality with females, as though he might be or should have been a girl too. As a very small boy the patient lost his father and began to identify onesidedly with his mother: when she later remarried, the stepfather became a potential lover instead of a true father-figure. The patient's relationships with his four younger siblings have been fraught with tremendous anxiety due to a conflict between physically protecting or destroying them.

Since the time of his father's death, this patient has been unable to speak properly in the presence of other people. He is a bad stutterer. His words come out fluently only when he sings, whispers, or talks strangely, as with an affected dialect. He has managed to make this defect into something of an asset: for instance, his mannerisms make him the life of the party when it comes to telling jokes in a foreign accent, singing folk songs, or impersonating women. But at work and in other more serious activity he is very handicapped. Many aspects of his communicative behavior besides speech are disturbed; he walks and moves with feminine gestures, and often uses a piping, high-pitched, girlish voice.

The patient has become extremely selfconscious over his speech nonfluency and thinks that certain phonemes "give" him particular difficulty. When asked to single these out, he exemplifies this by mentioning words that are far more notable for their loaded meaning than for their phonetic complexity; for instance, "I have trouble with the words *baby, surgery,* and any words that begin with W *(double you)*." Also, he focuses a good deal of attention on his breathing, and blames "a catch in diaphragmatic respiration" rather than an emotional problem for the soundmaking disturbance.

A noxious complication of this patient's pathology is that many of his friends think his behavior is "cute." Therefore he does not hesitate to use disturbed soundmaking to attract other sexually undifferentiated people. He advertises his immaturity by stuttering, and seduces people by sounding hesitant, halting, and apparently helpless. Greatly in need of true sympathy and understanding, he manipulates his homosexual partners by feigning to be intensely fond of them. When he makes a conquest he keeps his mouth busy with seemingly endless kissing, biting, and sucking of the lover. Besides thus satisfying his tremendous oral craving, this erotic activity also prevents speech and thereby spares the patient from having to talk about himself. Problems arise however as soon as he and his lover are spent physically, for they then experience the need to get to know one another personally, and this may call for talking. Now the patient is blocked; he cannot truthfully verbalize how he feels about his stunted development or about his rage towards others. Words get stuck in his throat; if they are spoken at all, it is often with such rapidity that the listener cannot follow, or so lethargically that one falls asleep.

Psychotherapy presents both a challenge and a dilemma for this patient: he must deal verbally with his problems, but is usually blocked in this effort precisely at the very moment that he tries to be truthful about himself. When he wants direct contact and immediate relief of physical tensions, speech provides him only distance, delay, and further frustration. His answer to this is prolonged emotive soundmaking. Hour after hour is whiled away with jabber about artificial, trivial, or emotionally tantalizing topics; he is fluent—indeed superfluent—by using effeminacy, baby talk, and defensive mannerisms. If confronted with reality and asked to face his deeper sense of isolation and anguish, he cannot talk, but stammers and stutters. For example, after meeting someone who reminded him of his youngest brother, the patient ecstatically raved about this new boyfriend, describing his physical attributes in enthusiastic and glowing terms. So long as this topic dominated his thoughts and was reinforced through daily encounters with the new love object, the patient felt elated and spoke fluently. But his mother called up on the telephone one day. From that moment on the patient was unable to speak without a severe stammer. The previously beloved sexual partner now became a target for scorn and abuse. The patient had become aware of his jealousy toward his youngest brother for basking in the affection of both mother and stepfather. He was now flooded with overwhelming anger and further recalled scenes from childhood where he saw himself as unwanted, rejected, and unacknowledged.

Along with the deterioration of his speech goes a ravenous appetite for foods. As a youngster, this patient had often gorged himself in order to feel filled and to offset the frustration and tension occasioned by feeling unloved. This gluttony made him fat, lethargic, and acne-skinned. Consequently his natural attractiveness was diminished, he became less appealing and further lost the affection of his family and friends. Neither on the playground nor in the classroom was he able to compete successfully with other boys.

One way to compensate for his unhappy life is to dream, and he often portrays himself nocturnally as a girl, vividly dressed, who is irresistibly attractive. But often such dreams turn into nightmares, and unless he wakes up they go on to sadomasochistic castration scenes. Bloody stumps, mangled legs, maimed bodies, and other terrifying symbols then predominate, often with a soundtrack of horrible screaming. The patient likes to stimulate his fantasies by going to horror movies; a favorite is Hitchcock's "Psycho" which is about an insane transvestite killer, a young man who stutters.

A VIRGINAL PIANO PLAYER

This talented young lady aged twenty spends ten to twelve hours a day at her piano. Unless riveting herself thus to a practice bench, she feels compelled to run into the kitchen and eat. Scales and arpeggios really prevent her from downing entire loaves of bread and full quarts of milk. Sometimes the musical compulsion doesn't work. After giving in to her voracious appetite, she walks the streets with self-loathing, and avoids all human contact while daydreaming about a Prince Charming who will rescue her from this distress.

The patient's history is an unhappy one: both her parents are extremely frightened people who try to organize their lives around rituals. The father is a well-to-do oil man who uses business conferences and cocktail parties to absorb his anxiety. The mother is religiously devout, addicted to drugs, and cannot live in physical proximity to her husband. Unable to elicit love from her parents, the patient has turned to her teachers in school for advice and protection. Especially during adolescence did she excel scholastically and thereby ingratiate herself to find acceptance.

Her soundmaking pathology involves silence. Words she finds useless vehicles for communication; they seem like empty forms devoid of feeling. Anyway, to use the mouth is a terrible threat, because it reminds this patient that as a baby she was not well fed and was weaned too early. A compromise solution is musical soundmaking. She has chosen to play the piano, an instrument which for her symbolizes protection against a storm of unfulfilled needs and unexpressed emotions.

An additional benefit of music is that one of her Prince Charmings comes with the piano—a kindly teacher who takes a devoted interest in pupils. For this patient the weekly visits to his studio are for other purposes than just music lessons. Like the girl victims in Ionesco's "The Lesson (59)," she seeks more than instruction about symbolic communication; she craves direct physical contact. This desire is partly gratified at each music lesson; teacher and pupil sit closely together and symbolically hold hands while interdigitating the keyboard with octave passages. Also there is the vicarious experience of a family, for the teacher has a charming wife who serves French pastry and coffee after each lesson, making the miserable girl feel accepted and at home. Nonverbal communication suffuses the atmosphere, from oversize, diaper-like napkins offered by the hostess, to the authoritative, emotive storytelling of the host.

For the patient this arrangement is most agreeable. She has no real lover and is content to bask in the warm approval of these pseudoparents. But the teacher and his wife see this situation as a threat, for they have biological children, and cannot really afford to feed another person. Also the teacher senses that this girl subtly undermines his authority as a musician in that she unconsciously expects him to step out of his professional role into that of a lover. Giving in to this silent, unspoken demand would require that he relinquish his primary function as her mentor and spiritual guide. The man understands that this would make him altogether too human and incapable of being adored.

The patient's acute psychotic decompensation resolves this dilemma, for the teacher must now see her as a disturbed soundmaker and no longer as a normal musician. He becomes concerned when the girl lapses into catatonic silence and runs away. He calls a psychiatrist who finds that she is morbidly withdrawn and apathetic. Her voice is flat, and while she forms her words carefully and pedantically arranges them into neat sentences, what she says is not related to what she feels. She sounds a little like a teletype machine, emitting signals that are detached from warmth and life. Occasionally she conveys her distress nonverbally with a grimace of disgust, a trembling foot, or a clammy handshake. She needs shelter and protective care before she can resume a normal life and improve her soundmaking.

A POLYGLOT MAGAZINE SALESMAN

His parents bring this seventeen year old high school student to the psychiatrist because they sense that his speech disturbances may indicate a serious personality disorder. The family has lived overseas for over half the patient's life, thus exposing him to several different language environments—mainly Oriental—in addition to his native English. The patient is proud of his fluency in foreign tongues, which he has learned through much speaking to household servants and other native employees of his father's insurance company. He is ashamed however of his soundmaking defects in English. He stutters particularly on words that begin with s, p, f, or d. These usually turn into endlessly repetitive sound chains, leaving the listener agog with expectancy and pity. After several attempts at speech he allows the words to disintegrate in his mouth, and stands momentarily silent, then blushes, gesticulates, and grimaces, while trying frantically to substitute other words that convey similar meanings but do not contain the dangerous consonants.

Emotional factors are plainly in evidence: for example, the soundmaking disturbance only appears when he must speak with intimates, or to persons who are his superiors in age and experience. He stutters very badly in the presence of his parents, close friends, and the psychiatrist. But in situations of anonymity, or where he can imagine himself to be superior to the listener, he speaks very well. This may account for his extraordinary success in nonpersonal situations: he was a high school cheerleader and recently became student body president. He also excels in his vacation job, soliciting magazine subscriptions by going from house to house. Here he must talk fast, aggressively, and often argumentatively, and he seldom stutters.

The patient's speech developed normally until a younger sibling came along, a girl who was braindamaged at birth and subsequently developed spasticity. The boy resented all the attention she got because of her physical defects, and began to mimic her organic speech, in part to ridicule her but also because this focussed more attention onto him. While he is already taller than his father and at an age when his overseas pals get married and have children, this patient feels he must abstain from all forms of sexual release, even masturbation and wetdreams.

This rigid attitude is based partly on overcompliance to puritanical ideas stemming from his parents, and is also due to his tendency for taking literally what he hears about how to behave.

Exposure to different cultures and to varying codes of conduct has produced, in this patient, a curiously flexible inflexibility: he feels bound to conform rigidly to what he is told, no matter what he has been told before. He does not think of words as symbolic sounds uttered for communicative purposes which can initiate, control, or delay actions. Rather, in his mind words and actions are inextricably linked, and he fears that to speak about something might directly bring it about. When he tries to "d-d-d-discuss p-p-prostitution" for example, he immediately sees his mother interfering with his sexual activity, stops the discussion, and then verbally attacks the "cruder aspects" of life. It is interesting that he can swear in several languages, but not in English—his mother-tongue—which must be kept clean.

Speech for this patient is a matter primarily of doing or of not doing something. He is intrigued with the physical processes of soundmaking, about which he knows a good deal. He is more interested in how he speaks—fast or slow, smoothly or haltingly, clear or mushy—than in what he says, since topics for conversation are already carefully classified in his mind according to what is and what is not "good" to talk about. The same thing happens when he reads: compulsively he looks behind each word to puzzle about "hidden" meanings. For fear that his own words might reveal hidden fantasies, he never writes anything down. Yet he likes to use a typewriter—this instrument apparently gives him more control and mastery over words than does the unaided hand. Furthermore, the typewriter is also a weapon against members of his family, whom he keeps awake at night with its noisy activity.

Paradoxically, the patient also inhibits himself so far as emotive soundmaking is concerned; he considers emotional behavior in general with distaste, and can only cry, shout, embrace, and kiss when he is intoxicated or very fatigued. Occasionally he invites friends to his house for all-night parties, which after much drinking, wrestling, and dancing brings about some release of emotional tension. At other times he locks himself into a room, and for hours turns somersaults and lifts weights. The patient very much fears his own aggressive impulses, and for good reason, since when he lets himself go he can become very belligerent, and even dangerous to himself. Once after an interview with his psychiatrist he misinterpreted something the doctor said and temporarily turned all his inhibitions off with the slogan "to slow down is unhealthy." He then drove his car at maniacal speeds, ran through a number of red lights, and angrily (without stuttering) denounced a policeman who tried to stop him. The following night he slept fitfully and dreamt: "a man lines my father, mother, and little sister up against a tree and kills them—maybe I get killed, too."

A SCREECHY INTERIOR DECORATOR

This strikingly redhaired lady has carved out a very successful business career. She is fifty years old—an outstanding interior decorator—and she supports her husband and his three children. But in her emotional life she is something of a failure. She has consulted many psychiatrists and now seeks help again because an unrelievable sense of doom seems to haunt her waking thoughts, and during each night she is beset with terrifying nightmares of catastrophe and ruin. The death of a close friend precipitated this depression. In addition, there is a problem of which she does not speak: her inability to speak normally. Every few seconds she spasmodically constricts her throat, producing an unpleasant, gurgling noise. Also she stammers, and her voice is unusually high-pitched, strident, sharp, and nasalized. This pathologic soundmaking has been in evidence since early childhood; several forms of speech therapy have failed to produce any lasting improvement.

"Control" is the patient's motto for life and work. She rigidly exerts control over herself, throttling mostly any tendency to be passive, feminine, and helpless. At the same time she tries to control the behavior of other people, and much of her present difficulty stems from a belated awareness that this often is impossible. She tries to gain control over others by appearing affectionate, and by helpfully applying her superior intelligence to their problems. One reason why this fails is that her abominable soundmaking advertises that she cannot solve her own problems. No matter how hard she tries, it is impossible for her to control all autonomic processes. Breathing and vocalization will always reflect the emotions, and this is where this woman is in trouble. The more effort she makes, the less smooth her soundmaking becomes; thus with each increase of willfulness her communication worsens.

It is interesting to see how the patient has kept going in spite of these difficulties. Neither her present husband nor her deceased close friend were adept speakers. They depended on her agressiveness and overlooked her defective capacity for warm and spontaneous human relationships. Taking advantage of her helpfulness, they ignored the uproarious soundmaking, or were amused by it. But two previous husbands and four children have not been able to tolerate this patient's noisy, manipulative, and aggressive ways so well. Over the years they have managed to live at a considerable distance from her, and the family visits her only at unavoidable anniversary and formal occasions.

Having gradually become a psychiatric invalid, this patient now bears the scars of chronic soundmaking pathology. Her grunting only vaguely hints at the pain and hurt that she early experienced in a fatherless home, where her insecure and love-starved mother drove the girl prematurely into competitive relationships with men. Success in these early adolescent work relationships in stores and business offices was often purchased with sexual favors, bestowed on her male co-workers at the expense of pride and individuality. Her language function, while it improved semantically, gradually deteriorated on the phonologic level where feelings are communicated. Her broken voice has been crusted over with linguistic scar-tissue, and her speech exemplifies the saynothing utility of clichés (125). The friendship whose disruption by death brought the patient to a psychiatrist had been a sticky twoperson mutual-admiration society. The friend was a pharmacist who gave her drugs in exchange for support. She provided him with social contacts, money, a feeling of prestige, and flowery expressions of respect.

This psychopathology presents a terrible risk for any psychotherapist who tries to get behind the patient's verbal defensiveness for a look at the smouldering wounds of childhood traumata. Tampering with her soundmaking abnormality tends to provoke rapid shifts to body language. For instance, one day she may speak of "the diaper business" and the next day come down with a dehydrating diarrhea. In the face of an obvious problem with the menopause, this patient persists in denying her femaleness and more vehemently tries to behave like a man. Ingenuously she states "I miss menstruation like I miss having a rock in my shoe!" Ill health keeps her legitimately in contact with members of the medical profession, and she has the money to pay for any sympathy obtained from doctors. For revenge upon an unsympathetic physician she can turn her suffering into a weapon. Like a female Don Juan, this patient has a long list of victims; she can catalogue grievances against many outstanding practitioners in the community. Yet in some sense all her complaining is justified, for no physician has yet been able to relieve this patient's misery.

SUMMARY

The four patients presented in this chapter can speak, but they have severe conflicts about the use of the mouth for communicative behavior. Often this leads to silence, stuttering, and other forms of speech pathology. The first patient is an immature, sexually-confused man whose almost constant search for direct oral gratification interfered with his soundmaking. The second patient is a music student who became abnormally withdrawn, silent and hungry when her teacher failed to reciprocate her love. The third patient is a multilingual man who had difficulty expressing hostile and erotic ideas through words, particularly in his native language. The fourth patient is a controlling, masculine-protest type of woman who covered up depressive feelings and sought help for secondary psychosomatic complaints. Such patients often seem to rely on their speech pathology as a means for regulating emotional rapport between themselves and listeners. At times they speak well, at other times the speech impediment resembles part of an intractable habit. This is why I would question the value of speech exercises, training, or other forms of direct rehabilitation for such patients, unless this is accompanied by psychotherapy aimed at underlying interpersonal insecurities and fears.

CODA

In these eleven chapters I have presented an approach to the study of human soundmaking which hopefully can be applied to further investigation of this important aspect of communication. A lot of ground has been covered — from historical factors in the regulation of acoustic behavior to the morphology of sounds emitted by individuals. But much is left unexplored. The search for correlation between acoustical and behavioral variables, as outlined in Chapters 7 and 8, has only just begun. Already my colleagues in this new field of investigation are hard at work to do more and better studies of this kind. We are held back by limitations in our methods for measuring and analyzing human sounds, and this is where help from engineers and acousticians is badly needed. As I write these lines my desk is already cluttered with spectrograms which reveal far more acoustic detail than do the half-octave band analyses reported in this book. Linguists and phoneticians are needed to assist in the interpretation of such data.

Yet improved acoustic and linguistic methods will not automatically give us answers to the many difficult questions about communication of emotion which this book has raised. What is equally necessary is a reexamination of our psychiatric concepts of emotional states, together with a clarification of the clinical nomenclature for emotionality. We already have excellent descriptive terms — depression, anger, excitement, confusion, ambivalence, fear, and many others; and we attempt through adjectives like acute, chronic, reactive, and recurrent to hook these descriptive terms into a time scheme. But this is as yet terribly imprecise. It will be necessary — as we perfect our methods for measuring sounds— also to spell out the precise nature of an emotional state under investigation, to find ways of grading its intensity, to allow for the coexistence and overlapping of other emotions, and to specify the duration of each. This is a challenge for physiologists who can instrumentally perceive the biological undercurrents of emotion before these reach the effector organs and become manifest as internal symptoms. It is a problem for psychiatrists and clinical psychologists trained to recognize the external manifestations of emotional disturbance. And it requires the help of psychoanalysts skilled in the evaluation of emotional states by reference to dreams, fantasies, verbal thoughts, and other emotionally tinged products of mental activity.

All of this will take a long time. Meanwhile what we already know intuitively about soundmaking should be the subject for further scientific inquiry. I mentioned, in Chapters 2 and 4, some of the characteristic sounds emitted by human beings. The fact that we have verbal labels for these acoustic phenomena — cries, screams, babbling, etc. — indicates that they are sufficiently discrete manifestations of behavior to be picked by ear out of the total fabric of human soundmaking. Yet surprisingly little work has been done to study objectively even these imperfect bridge concepts between emotion and soundmaking. If you doubt my words, just open a dozen authoritative texts about voice and speech and try to find even one sentence about laughter, a ubiquitous and pleasurable form of human soundmaking whose relationship to psychopathology is quite unclear.

Today we stand in great danger of being dehumanized, or actually annihilated by discoveries which intellectual pursuit has brought about. Isn't it time that we study ourselves a bit more closely? There is much yet to be discovered in us, in our behavior towards one another, and in our group activities. Sounds that we make while alone and together, what these mean, and how they are used for emotional communication is but one fruitful area for scientific pursuit.

BIBLIOGRAPHY

1. ALEXANDER, R. D.: Sound communication in orthoptera and cidadidae, in *Animal Sounds and Communication* (Lanyon, W. E. and Tavolga, W. N., editors) Am. Inst. Biol. Sci., Washington D. C., 1960, 443 pp.

2. ALSTON, E. F.: Psychoanalytic psychotherapy conducted by correspondence; report of therapy with a patient hospitalized for tuberculosis, *Int. J. Psychoan., 38*:32-50, 1957.

3. BARBARA, D. A.: *Your Speech Reveals Your Personality*, Springfield, Thomas, 1958, 174 pp.

4. BARBARA, D. A.: *The Art of Listening*, Springfield, Thomas, 1958, 201 pp.

5. BARBARA, D. A. (ed.): *Psychological and Psychiatric Aspects of Speech and Hearing*, Springfield, Thomas, 1960, 756 pp.

6. BARTOLI, D.: *Del Suono de'tremori Armonici*, Rome, 1679, Frank De Bellis Collection.

7. BARZUN, J.: *Berlioz and His Century*, New York, Meridian Books, 1956, 448 pp.

8. BATESON, G.: Minimal Requirements for a theory of Schizophrenia, *Arch. Gen. Psychiatry, 2*:477-491, 1960.

9. BEKESY, G. VON, and ROSENBLITH, W. A.: The early history of hearing—Observations and Theories, *J. Acoust. Soc. Am., 20*: 727-748, 1948.

10. BEKESY, G. VON: *Experiments in Hearing*, New York, McGraw-Hill, 1960, 745 pp.

11. BERANEK, L.: *Acoustics*, New York, McGraw-Hill, 1954, 481 pp.

12. BERNFELD, S.: Freud's earliest theories and the school of Helmholtz, *Yearbook of Psychoan., 1*:31-47, 1945.

13. BETTMAN, O. L.: *A Pictorial History of Medicine*, Springfield, Thomas, 1956, 318 pp.

14. BIRD, B.: *Talking with Patients*, Philadelphia, Lippincott, 1955, 154 pp.

15. BLOOMFIELD, L.: *Language*, New York, Holt & Co., 1933, 564 pp.

16. BROADBENT, D. E.: Effects of Noise on Behavior, Ch. 10 in *Hand-*

book of Noise Control, (Harris, C. M. editor), New York, Mc-Graw-Hill, 1957, 1031 pp.

17. BRODY, E. B., NEWMAN, R., and REDLICH, F. C.: Sound recording and the problem of evidence, *Science, 113*:379-380, 1951.

18. BROWN, R.: *Words and Things*, Glencoe, The Free Press, 1958, 398 pp.

19. BROWN, R. and FRASER, C.: The acquisition of syntax, to appear as a Child Development Monograph, (Kessen, W., editor).

20. BUEHLER, K.: *Die Sprachtheorie*, Jena, Fischer, 1934, 434 pp.

21. CANTRIL, H. and ALLPORT, G.: *The Psychology of Radio*, New York, Harper, 1935.

22. CLOUDSLEY-THOMPSON, J.: *Rhythmic Activity in Animal Physiology and Behavior*, New York, Academic Press, 1961, 236 pp.

23. Committee on Nomenclature and Statistics of the American Psychiatric Association, *Diagnostic and Statistical Manual-Mental Disorders*, Washington, D. C., APA, 1952, 132 pp.

24. DARWIN, C.: *The Expression of the Emotions in Man and Animals*, New York, Philosophical Library, 1955, 372 pp.

25. DAVIDSON, G.: Medico-legal aspects of infanticide, *J. Crim. Psychopathology, 2*:500-511, 1941.

26. DIETHELM, O.: *Treatment in Psychiatry*, Springfield, Thomas, 1955, 545 pp.

27. DISERENS, C. M.: *The Influence of Music on Behavior*, New Jersey, Princeton Univ. Press, 1926.

28. DORN, H. F.: World Population Growth: an international dilemma, *Science, 135*:283-290, 1962.

29. DOUTHWAITE, A. H. (ed.): *French's Index of Differential Diagnosis*, Baltimore, Williams & Wilkins, 7th edition, 1954, 1046 pp.

30. DURANT W. and DURANT, A.: *The Age of Reason Begins*, New York, Simon and Schuster, 1961, 732 pp.

31. EINSTEIN, A.: *A Short History of Music*, New York, Knopf, 1938, 438 pp.

32. EISENBERG, L., ASCHER, E., and KANNER, L.: A Clinical Study of Gilles de La Tourette's Disease (Maladie des Tics) in Children, *Am. J. Psychiatry, 115*:715-723, 1959.

33. ESSEN. O. VON: Die phonetische Dokumentation der Nasalität und des offenen Näselns, *Folia phoniat., 13*:269-275, 1961.

34. EVANS, B.: But What's a Dictionary for? *The Atlantic Monthly, 209*:57-62, 1962.

35. FANT, G.: *Acoustic Theory of Speech Production*, 's-Gravenhage, Mouton & Co., 1960, 323 pp.

36. FARBER, D. J.: Written communication in psychiatry, *Psychiatry 16*: 365-374, 1953.

37. FELDMAN, S.: *Mannerisms of Speech and Gestures in Everyday Life,* New York, Int. Univ. Press, 1959, 301 pp.

38. FENICHEL, O.: *The Psychoanalytic Theory of Neurosis,* New York, 1945, Norton, 703 pp.

39. FERENCZI, S.: Psychogenic anomalies of voice production, in *Further Contributions to the Theory and Technique of Psychoanalysis,* London, Hogarth Press, 1950, pp, 105-109.

40. FLACH, F. F. and REGAN, P. F. III: *Chemotherapy in Emotional Disorders,* New York, McGraw-Hill, 1960, 314 pp.

41. FLEISCHER, O.: *Neumen-Studien,* Leipzig, 1895, 3 vol.

42. FLETCHER, H.: *Speech and Hearing in Communication,* Princeton, Von Nostrand, 1953, 461 pp.

43. FREUD, S.: Papers on Psychoanalytic Technique, in *Collected Papers of Sigmund Freud,* vol. 2 (trans. J. Riviere), London, Hogarth Press, 1946, 404 pp.

44. FREUD, S.: *An Outline of Psychoanalysis* (trans. J. Strachey), New York, Norton, 1949, 127 pp.

45. FREUD, S.: *Three Essays on the Theory of Sexuality* (trans. J. Strachey), London, Imago, 1952, 133 pp.

46. GARDINER, W.: *The Music of Nature,* Boston, Wilkins and Carter, 1838.

47. GEDDA, L., FIORI-RATTI, L., et BRUNO, G.: La voix chez les jumeaux monozygotiques, *Folia phoniat., 12*:81-94, 1960.

48. GLAUBER, I. P.: The psychoanalysis of stuttering, in *Stuttering— A Symposium,* (Eisenson, J., editor) pp. 72-119, New York, Harper & Bros., 1958, 402 pp.

49. GRAY, C. and HESELTINE, P.: *Carlo Gesualdo—Prince of Venosa, Musician and Murderer,* London, MacVeagh, 1926, 145 pp.

50. GREENBERG, J. H.: Historical linguistics and unwritten languages, in *Anthropology Today* (Kroeber, A. L., editor) pp. 265-286, Univ. of Chicago Press, 1953, 966 pp.

51. HARRIS, C. (editor): *Handbook of Noise Control,* New York, McGraw-Hill, 1957, 1031 pp.

52. HAYES, A. S.: Paralanguage and Kinesics: Pedagological perspectives, in *Approaches to Semiotics,* (Sebeok, T. and Hayes, A., editors) s'Gravenhage, Mouton & Co. in press 1963.

53. HEDIGER, H. P.: The evolution of territorial behavior, in *Social Life of Early Man,* (Washburn, S. L., editor) Chicago, Aldine Co., 1961, 279 pp.

54. HELMHOLTZ, H.: *On the Sensations of Tone as a Physiological Basis*

for the Theory of Music, 1885, 576 pp. (reprinted 1954 by Do-
ver Publications, New York).

55. HENDERSON, I.: Ancient Greek Music, Ch. 9 in *Ancient and
Oriental Music,* (Wellesz, E., editor), London, Oxford Univ.
Press, 1957, 530 pp.

56. HOCKETT, C. F.: The Origin of Speech, *Scientific American,* Sept.
1960, pp. 89-96.

57. HODEIR, A.: *Since Debussy: A View of Contemporary Music,* New
York, Grove Press, 1961, 256 pp.

58. HUGHES, G. W. and HALLE, M.: On the recognition of speech by
machine, pp. 252-256 in *Information Processing,* Paris,
UNESCO, 1960.

59. IONESCO, E.: The Lesson, pp. 44-78 in *Four Plays* (trans. Allen,
D. M.) New York, Grove, 1958, 160 pp.

60. IRWIN, O. C.: Infant speech: Consonant sounds according to
manner of articulation, *J. Speech Disorders, 12*:397-401, 1947.

61. JONES, E.: *The Life and Work of Sigmund Freud,* New York,
Basic Books, 3 vol., 1953, 1955, 1957.

62. KARELITZ, S.: *Infant vocalizations,* phonograph record, CL 2669 A
(Long Island Jewish Hospital).

63. KNAPP, P. H.: The ear, listening, and hearing, *J. Am. Psychoan. A.,
1*:672-689, 1953.

64. KOENINGSBERGER, L.: *Hermann von Helmholtz* (trans. Welby),
London, Oxford Univ. Press, 1906, 440 pp.

65. KOESTLER, A.: *The Sleepwalkers—A History of Man's Changing
Vision of the Universe,* New York, MacMillan, 1959, 624 pp.

66. KRAMER, E.: The judgment of personal characteristics and emotions from nonverbal properties of speech, Ann Arbor, University of Michigan, ORA Project 04411, 1962.

67. KRIS, E.: On preconscious mental processes, *Psychoan. Quarterly,
19*:540-560, 1950.

68. KURTZ, J. H.: *The sounds of a day-old baby,* Tape-recording available from Langley Porter Neuropsychiatric Institute, San Francisco.

69. LA BARRE, W.: *The Human Animal,* Univ. Chicago Press, 1954,
372 pp.

70. LANGER, S. K.: *Philosophy in a New Key,* New York, Mentor Books,
1948, 248 pp.

71. LEVIN, N. M. (editor): *Voice and Speech Disorders: Medical Aspects,* Springfield, Thomas, 1962, 1108 pp.

72. LEWIS, M. M.: *Infant Speech—A Study of the Beginnings of Language,* New York, Harcourt Brace & Co., 1936, 335 pp.

73. LICKLIDER, J. C. R.: Basic correlates of the auditory stimulus, Ch. 25 in *Handbook of Experimental Psychology* (Stevens, S. S. editor), New York, Wiley & Sons, 1951, 1436 pp.

74. LOWINSKY, E. E.: *Secret Chromatic Art in the Netherlands Motet,* New York, Columbia Univ. Press, 1946, 184 pp.

75. LOWINSKY, E. E.: Music in the culture of the Renaissance, *J. Hist. Ideas, 15*:509-553, 1954.

76. LUCHSINGER, R. and ARNOLD, G. E.: *Lehrbuch der Stimm-und Sprachheilkunde,* Wien, Springer, 1959, 731 pp.

77. LYNIP, A. W.: The use of magnetic devices in the collection and analysis of the preverbal utterances of an infant, *Genet. psychol. monogr., 44*:221-262, 1951.

78. MacLEAN, P. D., ROBINSON, B. W., and PLOOG, D. W.: Experiments on localization of genital function in the brain, *Trans. Am. Neurol. Assoc.,* 1959, pp. 105-109.

79. MAEDER, H.: *The Tongues of Tyrants,* Atlas, August 1962, pp. 92-99.

80. MEERLOO, J.: Rhythm in babies and adults, *Arch. Gen. Psychiat., 5*: 169-175, 1961.

81. MERRILL, B. R.: Childhood attitudes toward flatulence and their possible relation to adult character, *Yearbook of Psychoan., 8*: 213-224, 1952.

82. MOSES, P.: *The Voice of Neurosis,* New York, Grune and Stratton, 1954, 131 pp.

83. NORTHROP, F. S. C.: *The Meeting of East and West,* New York, MacMillan, 1946, 531 pp.

84. OLSEN, H. F.: *Acoustical Engineering,* Princeton, New Jersey, Van Nostrand, 1957, 718 pp.

85. OPIE, I. and OPIE, P.: *The Lore and Language of School Children,* London, Oxford Univ. Press, 1959, 417 pp.

86. OSTWALD, P. F. and REGAN, P. F. III: Psychiatric disorders associated with childbirth, *J. Nerv. Ment. Dis., 125*:153-165, 1957.

87. OSTWALD, P. F.: Human sounds, Ch. 6 in *Psychological and Psychiatric Aspects of Speech and Hearing* (Barbara, D., editor), Springfield, Thomas, 1960, 756 pp.

88. OSTWALD, P. F.: A method for the objective denotation of the sound of the human voice, *J. Psychosom. Res., 4*:301-305, 1960.

89. OSTWALD, P. F.: Visual denotation of human sounds, *Arch. Gen. Psychiatry, 3*:177-121, 1960.

90. OSTWALD, P. F.: The sounds of human behavior, *Logos, 3*:13-24, 1960.

91. OSTWALD, P. F.: Humming, sound and symbol, *J. Auditory Res., 3*: 224-232, 1961.

92. OSTWALD, P. F.: Sound, music, and human behavior, pp. 107-125 in *Music Therapy 1960* (Schneider, E., editor) NAMT, Kansas, 1962.

93. OSTWALD, P. F., FREEDMAN, D. G., and KURTZ, J. H.: Vocalization of infant twins, *Folia phoniat., 14*:37-50, 1962.

94. OSTWALD, P. F.: Behavior changes produced by selected acoustic stimuli, to appear in *Experimental Human Psychopathology*, (West, L. J., editor), P. Hoeber & Co.

95. PANCONCELLI-CALZIA, G.: Leonardo da Vinci und die Frage vom Sprechenden und Weinenden Foetus im Maerchenmotiv vom "Starken Knaben.", *Muenchener mediz. Wochenschrift, 96*: 1456-1458, 1954.

96. PARRISH, C.: *The Notation of Medieval Music*, New York, Norton, 1957, 228 pp.

97. PEAR, T. H.: *Voice and Personality as applied to Radio Broadcasting*, New York, Wylie, 1931, 247 pp.

98. PEI, M.: *One Language for the World and how to achieve it*, New York, Devin-Air, 1958, 291 pp.

99. PESCE, G.: "Acoustic Vases" Found in Sardinia, *J. Acoust. Soc. Am., 34*:134, 1962.

100. PINCHERLE, M.: *An Illustrated History of Music*, New York, Reynal & Co., 1959, 221 pp.

101. PITTENGER, R. E., HOCKETT, C. F., and DANEHY, J. J.: *The First Five Minutes—A Sample of Microscopic Interview Analysis*, Ithaca, Paul Martineau, 1960, 264 pp.

102. PLATO: CRATYLUS, from *The Dialogues of Plato*, Oxford Univ. Press, (trans. Jowett, B.) 1st edn. 1871, 3rd edn. 1892.

103. POTTER, R. K., KOPP, G. A. and GREEN, H. C.: *Visible Speech*, New York, Van Nostrand, 1947.

104. POETZL, O., ALLERS, R., TELER, J. and FISCHER, C.: Classical studies of preconscious stimulation in dreams, associations, and images, *Psychological Issues, 2*:1-156, 1960.

105. RANGELL, L.: The psychology of poise—with a special elaboration on the psychic significance of the snout or peri-oral region, *Int. J. Psychoan., 35*:313-332, 1954.

106. REVESZ, G.: *The Origin and Prehistory of Language*, London, Longmans Green, 1956, 240 pp.

107. ROOSE, L. J.: The influence of psychosomatic research on the psychoanalytic process, *J. Am. Psychoanal. Assoc., 8*:317-334, 1960.

108. RUESCH, J.: Nonverbal language and therapy, *Psychiatry, 18*:323-330, 1955.

109. RUESCH, J. and KEES, W.: *Nonverbal Communication—Notes on the Visual Perception of Human Relations,* Berkeley, Univ. Calif. Press, 1956, 205 pp.

110. RUESCH, J.: *Therapeutic Communication,* New York, Norton, 1961, 480 pp.

111. SACHS, C.: *The History of Musical Instruments,* New York, Norton, 1940, 505 pp.

112. SCHNEIDER, M.: Primitive Music, Ch. 1 in *Ancient and Oriental Music,* (Wellesz, E., editor), London, Oxford Univ. Press, 1957, 530 pp.

113. SCOTT, H. H.: Noise Measuring Techniques, Ch. 17 in *Handbook of Noise Control* (Harris, C., editor), New York, McGraw-Hill, 1957, 1031 pp.

114. SCOTT, J. E.: Roman Music, Ch. 10 in *Ancient and Oriental Music,* London, Oxford Univ. Press, 1957, 530 pp.

115. SCOTT, W. C. M.: Noise, speech and technique, *Int. J. Psychoan., 39*:1-4, 1958.

116. SEBEOK, T. A. and HAYES, A. S. (editors) : *Approaches to Semiotics,* s'Gravenhage, Mouton & Co. (in press) 1963.

117. SELYE, H.: *The Stress of Life,* New York, McGraw-Hill, 1956, 324 pp.

118. SIEGEL, S.: *Nonparametric Statistics for the Behavioral Sciences,* New York, McGraw-Hill, 1956, 312 pp.

119. SKINNER, B. F.: *Verbal Behavior,* New York, Appleton-Century-Crofts, 1957, 478 pp.

120. SONTAG, L. W. and WALLACE, R. F.: The response of the human foetus to sound stimuli, *Child Development, 6*:253-258, 1935.

121. SOROKIN, P. A.: *Fluctuation of Forms of Art,* vol. 1 of *Social and Cultural Dynamics,* New York, Bedminster, 1937, 745 pp.

122. STANKIEWICZ, E.: Problems of emotive language, in *Approaches to Semiotics* (Sebeok, T. and Hayes, A., editors), in press 1963.

123. STARKWEATHER, J. A.: Measurement of Vocal Behavior, Progress Report, USPHS Grant MY-3375, 1962.

124. STEELE, R.: *The Tattler,* London, April 1, 1710.

125. STEIN, M. H.: The cliché: a phenomenon of resistance, *J. Am. Psychoan. Assoc., 6*:263-277, 1958.

126. STEVENS, S. S.: Calculation of the loudness of complex noise, *J. Acoust. Soc. of Am., 28*:807-832, 1956.

127. STEVENS, S. S.: The direct estimation of sensory magnitudes-loudness, *Am. J. Psychol., 69*:1-25, 1956.

128. STEVENS, S. S.: The psychophysics of sensory function, Ch. 1 (pp. 1-33) in *Sensory Communication* (Rosenblith, W., editor), Cambridge, M.I.T. Press, 1961, 844 pp.

129. SULLIVAN, H. S.: Obituary of Edward Sapir 1884-1939, *Psychiatry, 2*:159, 1939.

130. SULLIVAN, H. S.: *The Psychiatric Interview* (Perry, H. S. and Gawel, M. L., editors), New York, Norton, 1954, 246 pp.

131. SWETS, J. A.: Is there a sensory threshold?, *Science, 134*:168-177, 1961.

132. SZASZ, T. S.: *The Myth of Mental Illness: Foundations for a theory of personal conduct,* New York, Hoeber-Harper, 1961, 337 pp.

133. SZUREK, S. A.: *The Roots of Psychoanalysis and Psychotherapy,* Springfield, Thomas, 1958, 134 pp.

134. TEIRICH, H. R. (editor): *Musik in der Medizin,* Stuttgart, Fischer, 1958, 207 pp.

135. TERVOORT, B. T.: Esoteric symbolism in the communication behavior of young deaf children, *Am. Annals of the Deaf, 106*:436-480, 1961.

136. WALTER, B.: *Thema und Variationen,* Frankfurt/Main, S. Fischer, 1960, 462 pp.

137. WEINSTEIN, E. A.: *Cultural Aspects of Delusion, a psychiatric study of the Virgin Islands,* Free Press of Glencoe, New York, 1962, 215 pp.

138. WENTWORTH, H. and FLEXNER, S. B.: *Dictionary of American Slang,* New York, Crowell, 1960, 669 pp.

139. WESSEL, F. T.: The Affektenlehre in the 18th Century, Ph. D. thesis, Indiana University, 1955.

140. WILMER, H. A.: An auditory sound association technique, *Science, 114*:621-622, 1951.

141. WINITZ, H.: Spectrographic investigation of infant vowels, *J. Genet. Psychol., 96*:171-181, 1960.

142. YERGES, L. F. and WEISLER, R. L.: Anti-Noise Ordinances, Ch. 39, in *Handbook of Noise Control,* (Harris, C. M., editor) New York, 1957, 1031 pp.

143. ZUBIN, J. (editor): *Field Studies in the Mental Disorders,* New York, Grune and Stratton, 1961, 495 pp.

GLOSSARY

"Words are the physicians of a disturbed mind."
AESCHYLUS: *Prometheus Bound*, c. 490 B.C.

acoustic(al): pertaining to the origins and physical properties of sound.

acoustics: the science of sound.

aesthetics: the science of beauty.

alto: tones occurring in the middle range of audible frequencies, usually associated with the female voice.

articulation: shaping of speech sounds by the throat and mouth.

auditory: pertaining to the reception of and the psychologic reactions to acoustic stimulation.

band: a specified segment of the frequency spectrum.

baritone: tones occurring in the low range of audible frequencies.

bass: the lowest range of vocal or instrumental tone.

clinical: pertaining to the individual study of patients.

clinician: one who studies and treats individual patients.

communication: a process whereby persons influence one another.

consonant: a speech sound produced by constriction or friction in the mouth or throat.

decibel: an acoustical unit which defines the ratio between two sound intensities in logarithmic form.

denotation: the specification of something in terms of its limits, contents, and significance.

denotative: pertaining to the specification and descriptive analysis of phenomena or experiences.

dental: a speech sound produced by the teeth.

diagnosis: a succinct denotative statement about a disease.

echolalia: echo-like repetition of a sound one has just heard.

embolophrasia: an intrusive sound like "ah", "er", "um", which is emitted while one hesitates or thinks about what to say next.

emotion: a physiologic condition experienced in terms of feelings rather than intellectually.

emotive: pertaining to a subjective, nonspecific, and expressive way for communicating ones feelings.

energy: the acoustical power of a sound expressed in kinetic, hydraulic, or electrical terms.

167

envelope: the growth, steady-state, decay, and duration characteristics of a sound.

experimental: pertaining to the study of behavior by means of trials made to confirm or disprove something doubtful.

expression: the direct externalization of feelings.

filter: a device which limits a sound to a certain range of frequencies along the spectrum.

flat voice: a human sound whose energy is spread across a wide band of the frequency spectrum.

formant: an energy-focus in the wide-band spectrographic analysis of speech.

frequency: the number of acoustic vibrations per second; cycles per second (cps).

fundamental: that element within a given sound whose vibratory frequency is numerically the smallest.

glottal: a speech sound produced by the larynx.

harmony: the orderly spatial aspects of an acoustic pattern.

hoarseness: a harsh voice quality related to laryngeal pathology.

hollow voice: a human sound of low intensity whose energy is predominantly carried by the fundamental tone.

information: whatever can be codified and transmitted by means of messages.

intensity: the rate of sound energy transmission through a unit area.

interview: that part of clinical study which does not involve manual, surgical, or other direct physical manipulation of the patient.

labial: a speech sound produced by the lips.

language: a system of symbols and the rules for organizing these into communicative patterns.

linguistic: pertaining to language.

linguistics: the study of (spoken) language.

listener: one who perceives sounds auditorily.

masking: raising the auditory threshold for one sound by the simultaneous production of another sound.

message: a communication sent by one person and received by another.

morphemes: nuclear semantic clusters of speech sound.

motant: a region of energy-concentration along the frequency spectrum when one applies half-octave band analysis to human sounds.

music: a pattern of sounds organized according to the dictates of a composer.

musicology: the study of music in terms of its history, symbolism, and meanings, rather than the technical aspects of performance.

myth: a fictitious story which is believed.

nasality: a voice quality related to resonance of the nose during speech.

neologism: a new word whose meaning is undefined.

neume: a symbol for the pitch, rhythm, and duration characteristics of vocal sound.

noise: (in acoustics) an unwanted sound; (in general) a disagreeable sound.

nonparametric statistics: statistical methods which make few assumptions about the nature of the population from which scores are taken.

nonverbal: pertaining to what cannot be codified in terms of spoken or printed words.

onomatopoeia: the emission of words which sound like what they denote, e.g. buzz, splash.

oral: pertaining to the mouth as an actual or symbolic tool for communication.

paralanguage: nonverbal acoustic behavior which accompanies, interrupts, or temporarily takes the place of speech.

patient: a sick person who becomes the object for clinical study and treatment.

pattern: an arrangement of individual components into one form.

personality: all the things that one can say about a person.

phon: the unit of loudness level, equivalent to decibels as measurable at 1,000 cps.

phonemes: speech sounds which function as symbols in the acoustic code of a language.

phonemic: pertaining to the acoustic code of a language.

phonetic: pertaining to the sounds of speech as actually made, rather than their meaning.

phonetics: the science of speech sounds.

pitch: an auditory attribute which depends primarily on the frequency characteristics of an acoustic stimulus.

preverbal: signs that one uses before learning to communicate with words.

pseudolanguage: verbalization which sounds like speech but is incomprehensible.

psychiatry: a branch of medicine dealing with disturbances in human behavior, thinking, and emotions.

psychoacoustics: the scientific study of auditory reactions.

psychoanalysis: a clinical approach to psychopathology which encourages the patient to study his own personality through free association.

psychology: the science of behavior.

psychopathology: clinically observable disturbances in human thinking, emotion, and behavior.

psychotherapy: the process whereby a physician reverses a patient's psychopathology through verbal interaction.

referential properties: the meanings of a word rather than its form or structure.

register: a specific range of the audible frequency spectrum.

research: painstaking investigation of something unknown.

resonance: the acoustical responses of one structure or cavity to sounds from another source.

rhythm: regularly recurrent temporal aspects of an acoustic pattern.

robust voice: a human sound of high intensity whose energy is focused into a narrow band at the center of the frequency spectrum.

scientific: pertaining to systematic observation, classification, and specification of phenomena.

semantic: pertaining to meaning as opposed to structure of language.

semantics: the study of meanings.

sender: one who emits signals.

sharp voice: a human sound whose energy is focussed into adjacent octave bands.

signal: an informative sign.

silence: the absence of sound.

sine wave: the vibratory characteristics of a pure single-frequency tone.

sone: an auditory loudness unit. A pure 1,000 cps tone of 40 decibels produces a loudness of one sone.

soprano: tones occurring in the high range of audible frequencies.

soundmaking: the intentional or unintentional production, by one or more persons, of acoustic impulses which may carry information to others.

sounds: acoustic vibrations which produce energy changes of the surrounding medium.

spectrogram: the visually plotted results of spectrographic analysis of a sound.

spectrograph: a device which analyzes sounds in terms of their energy distribution across the frequency spectrum over time.

spectrum: the range of frequencies pertinent in a particular context, e.g. 20-20,000 cps is the spectrum for human soundmaking.

speech: a pattern of sounds organized according to linguistic convention.

stammer: a halting, repetitious speech quality.

stereotype: a loosely framed concept which can be made to fit many individually varying patterns.

stuttering: speech which is halting, spasmodic, and repetitious.

symbol: something which stands for something else.

symptom: a sign of disease which the patient notices and complains about.

syndrome: a complex of symptoms which lead to a diagnosis.

synesthesia: overlap and fusion of information from different sources of sensory experience.

tenor: tones occurring in the middle range of audible frequencies, usually associated with the male voice.

threshold: the least amount of sound which can elicit a specified auditory sensation such as tone, noise, etc.

tone: an acoustic pattern containing a single vibratory frequency or a pattern of several frequencies which are related in terms of simple mathematical ratios.

unconscious: all the things about himself that a person does not know.

variability: the quality of being subject to inconstancy or variation.

velar: a speech sound produced by the soft palate.

verbal: pertaining to spoken or written words.

verbalization. fluent spontaneous speech.

vocal: pertaining to sounds whose energy stems from the lungs and larynx.

voice: a predominantly vocal sound.

vowel: an unobstructed vocal sound used in speech.

white noise: a sound whose energy output across all frequencies of the spectrum is uniform.

INDEX

A

Acoustic changes during psychotherapy, 84-95, 100, 108

Acoustic properties of sounds, x, 7, 10, 20, 32, 39, 47, 62

Acoustics, v, ix, 3, 7, 22, 24, 32, 35, 39, 55, 97, 129-130, 157, 167

Acoustic stereotypes, 59-83

Acoustic stimuli, 4, 10, 26, 114, 119, 124

Acting-out, 85, 88, 92, 146

Adaptation, 29

Adolescence, 20, 60, 65, 68, 72, 86, 133, 150, 155

Aeschylus, 167

Aesthetics, 7, 10, 167

Affectional needs, 95, 116, 133, 151, 154

Age of soundmakers, 43, 51, 108-110, 118

Aggression, 23, 59, 62, 64, 72, 79, 82, 85-88, 90, 95, 131, 147, 153, 155

Agitation, 72, 86, 120

Alarm Sounds, x, 13 (also see Signals)

Alcoholism, 74, 79, 86

Alexander, R. D., 159

Allers, R., 164

Alliteration, 130

Allport, G., 51, 160

Alphabet, 29-30, 123 (also see Phonemes; Phonetics)

Alston, E. F., 159

Alto, 6, 56, 167

Ambivalence, 74, 86, 92, 130

American Psychiatric Association, 110, 160

Anaclitic relationship, 95, 116

Anality, 142

Anechoic chamber, 28, 35

Anger, 65, 77, 89, 105, 116-117, 149, 154

Animal sounds, x, 6, 13-16, 32-33, 49, 115, 121, 123, 126, 134, 136

Annoyance, 46, 59, 70, 90, 117, 121

Anorexia nervosa, 73

Anxiety, 50, 64, 86, 130, 147, 150

Apathy, 78, 105, 151

Aphasia, 78, 117

Applause, 5, 19

Apraxia, 78

Arbitrariness, 15

Archeology, 3

Argumentation, 152

Arnold, G. E., 163

Arteriosclerosis, 75-76

Articulation, 18, 21, 30, 57, 65, 66, 73, 81, 143, 167

Artificiality, 149

Ascher, E., 160

Assaultiveness, 133

Assyria, 3

Attention, 14, 39, 141

Audiometry, 66

Auditory preferences, 125-127

Auditory projective test, 114-119

Auditory reactions, 9, 10, 14, 39, 46 (also see Listener)

Auditory sensations, 26, 43 (also see Effects of sound)

Auditory stimulation, 19, 24 (also see Acoustic stimuli)

Autism, 128-133

Autonomic processes, 154

Autonomy, 90

Autumn, S., vi

Awareness, 24, 154

B

Babbling, 19-20, 129

173

A